50 CIRCUITS USING 7400 SERIES IC's

ALSO BY THE SAME AUTHOR

BP36: 50 Circuits Using Germanium Silicon and Zener Diodes.
BP42: 50 Simple L.E.D. Circuits.

50 CIRCUITS
USING
7400 SERIES IC's

by
R. N. SOAR

BERNARD BABANI (publishing) LTD
THE GRAMPIANS
SHEPHERDS BUSH ROAD
LONDON W6 7NF
ENGLAND

Although every care is taken with the preparation of this book, the publishers or author will not be responsible in any way for any error that might occur.

I.S.B.N. 0 900162 77 5

First Published February 1979

Printed and Manufactured in Great Britain by C. Nicholls & Co. Ltd.

CONTENTS

Page

INTRODUCTION

This book contains 50 circuits using the 7400 and other 7400 series I.C.s.

The ultra low cost of I.C.s now means that the limitation on building circuits is not the cost of the active devices but the cost of associated capacitors, resistors and connecting wire.

The I.C.s 7400 and the 7413 are 14-pin D.I.L. I.C.s, i.e. "14 pin Dual In Line Integrated Circuits", pin 14 is the power connection or V+ and pin 7 is the power supply negative, ground or 0-volt connection. The power connections to pins 14 and 7 are not included on the diagrams to simplify the drawing but **don't forget to wire them up**, otherwise the circuit won't work! The circuits all function from a 4½-volt or 6-volt battery supply although the nominal voltage is 5 volts. A mains powered 5-volt stabilised supply is available from several sources. The savings on costs as against using batteries are vast.

Although some bargain price 7400 I.C.s are sold as "below standard" please remember that the standards set are very high. Part functional I.C.s are also available at very low cost. The 7400 is a four-gate I.C. (see diagram 1), but many circuits use only 2 or 3 gates so that a part functional I.C. can be used for these.

The four gates of a 7400 are identical:

Gate A pins 1, 2 inputs, pin 3 output
Gate B pins 4, 5 inputs, pin 6 output
Gate C pins 10, 9 inputs, pin 8 output
Gate D pins 13, 12 inputs, pin 11 output

The circuit diagram may show an oscillator using gates A and B but there is no reason why the oscillator cannot be built using gates A and C, B and C or C and D if the other gates are non-functional.

For permanent use the circuits can be soldered on 0.1″ matrix veroboard. A small bit 15W soldering iron is essential.

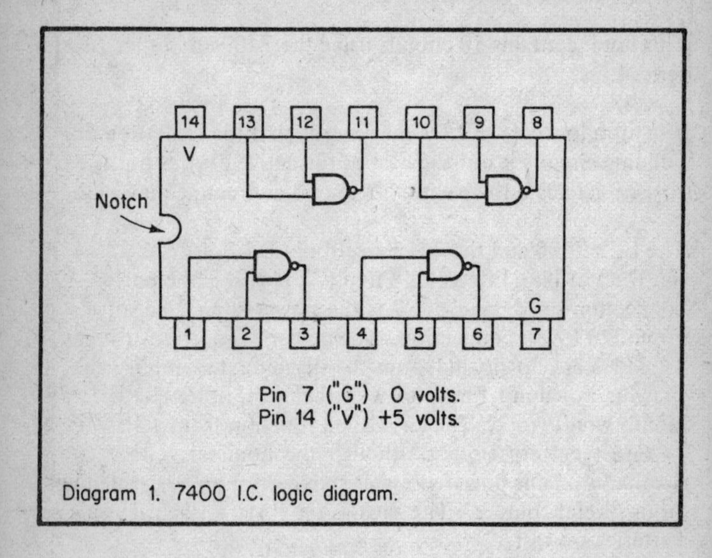

Diagram 1. 7400 I.C. logic diagram.

Diagram 1 shows the logic circuit of the 7400 I.C. Diagram 2 shows the logic symbol for one gate, each gate is a "Two Input NAND Gate".

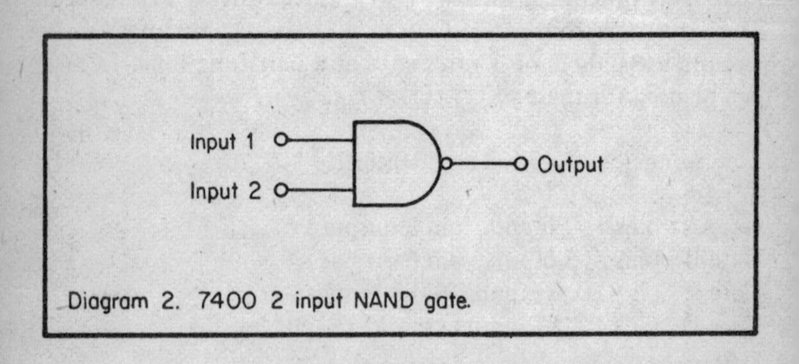

Diagram 2. 7400 2 input NAND gate.

The circuit diagram of a single gate is shown in diagram 3. The 7400 is a T.T.L. logic I.C., i.e. it uses "Transistor Transistor Logic". Each gate uses 4 transistors, each 7400 contains 4 x 4 = 16 transistors.

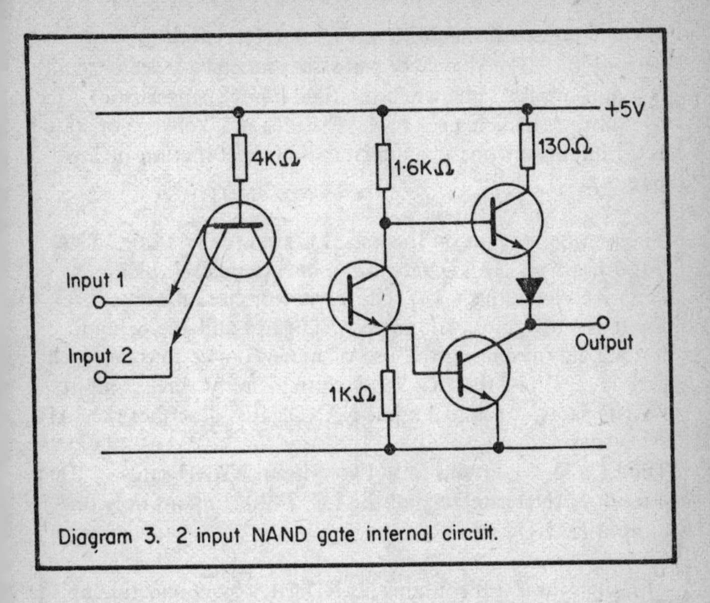

Diagram 3. 2 input NAND gate internal circuit.

The logic gates have two states, based on the binary system, 1 or "High" nominally 4 volts and 0 (zero) or "Low" nominally 0 volts. If a gate lead is unconnected this is equivalent to a 1 input, i.e. an unconnected gate lead is at "high" level. If a gate input lead is "grounded', i.e. connected to 0 volts the input is then 0.

The NAND gate is a "NOT AND" gate if both inputs (and function) are at logic 1, output is NOT 1. NOT 1 corresponds to zero, i.e. output is logic 0. If both inputs are logic 0, output is logic not 0, i.e. logic 1. It may be less easy to understand why the output is 1 when inputs are 0 and 1 or 1 and 0. However, consider it this way. The output with 2 inputs of 0 is 1. For a change of state an AND function has to take place, i.e. both inputs have to change for a change of state – this only occurs when both inputs change from 0 to 1. The 7400 gates are 2 input NAND gates but 3 input NAND gates 7410 I.C., 4 input NAND gates 7420 and even an 8 input NAND gate 7430 are available for the 7430 and its 8 input gate to change state each one of the 8 inputs must be either 1 or 0.

If the 8 inputs to the 7430 are 1,1,1,1,1,1,1,0 the output is 1. The change of state does not take place until all 8 inputs are the same when the final input changes from 0 to 1 the output then changes to 0. The idea of a "change of state" is an important one in understanding the function of logic circuits.

The number of pins on the logic I.C.s is usually 14 or 16. A 7400 has four NAND gates, 3 connections each plus power supply connections = 14. The larger number of inputs for 3 input NAND gates, 4 input NAND gates and the 8 input NAND gate requiring the use of more connections for each gate means that the I.C. 7410 contains only three 3-input NAND gates. "Triple 3 input NAND gate" describes the 7410.

The I.C. 7420 contains only two 4-input NAND gates – "Dual 4 input NAND gate" – and the I.C. 7430 contains only one 8-input NAND gate.

Although the 7400 contains NAND gates by connecting up the NAND gates in various ways, it is possible to form other types of gate:

(1) an inverter or "NOT" gate
(2) an AND gate
(3) an OR gate
(4) NOR gate.

The computer manufacturers use I.C.s specially made for the job. The 7402 is similar to the 7400 but contains four NOR gates. Just as NAND is "NOT AND", NOR is "NOT OR".

The 7400 is a very versatile I.C. as can be seen by the number of circuits in the applications manual. To help understand the function of a NAND gate a TRUTH table is shown for a 2 input NAND gate. Similar truth tables can be constituted for any logic gate. The truth table for an 8 input gate such as the 7430 is more complicated.

Logic	Pin 1 Input	Pin 2 Input	Pin 3 Output
	0	0	1
	1	0	1
	0	1	1
	1	1	0

2 input NAND gate truth table.

7400 Test Circuit (see diagram 4)

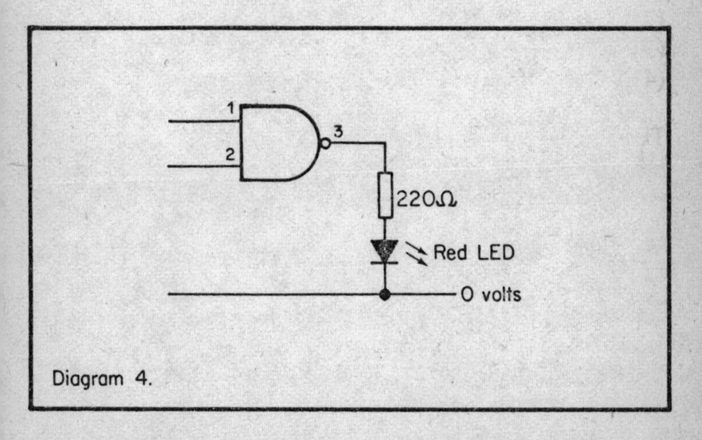

Diagram 4.

To test a 7400 I.C., connect power supply to pins 14 and 7.

With pins 1 and 2 unconnected the logic levels are inputs 1, 1, output 0. Connect pin 1 to 0 volts. Inputs are 1, 0, output 1 LED glows. Connect pin 2 to 0 volts (pin 1 disconnected). Inputs are 0, 1, output 1 LED glows. Connect pins 1 *and* 2 to 0 volts. Inputs are 0, 0, output 1 LED glows.

The red LED (light emitting diode) glows to indicate logic level 1. If LED is not illuminated this indicates logic level 0.

The test can be repeated with gates B, C and D.

Note to constructors: all the circuits shown use ¼W 5% resistors – all electrolytic capacitors are 16-volt working.

If a circuit is not working check the connections – a faulty I.C. is far less likely than faulty wiring.

Circuit One
INVERTER or NOT GATE

This circuit (see diagram 5) is the simplest possible and uses only one gate of a 7400. Pins 1 and 2 are connected together and the circuit functions as an inverter, i.e. the output is the opposite of the input.

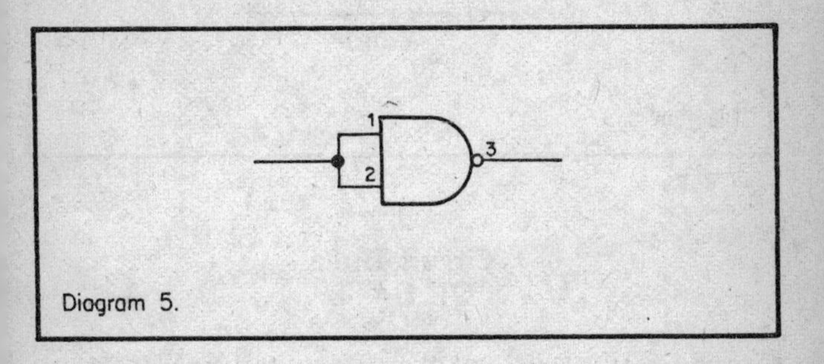

Diagram 5.

If the input is 0, out is 1. If the input is 1, output is 0.

As the circuit function is a negating one the gate is sometimes called a "NOT" gate. This expression is a better one. The term "inverter" is also used to mean a circuit using transistors or S.C.R.s to convert d.c. to a.c.

Circuit Two
AND GATE

As a NAND gate can be considered to be a "NOT AND" gate, if a "NOT" gate is placed after a NAND gate, the circuit becomes a "NOT NOT AND" gate. Two negatives make a positive (a principle common to mathematics and English grammar). The circuit is now an "AND" gate(see diagram 6).

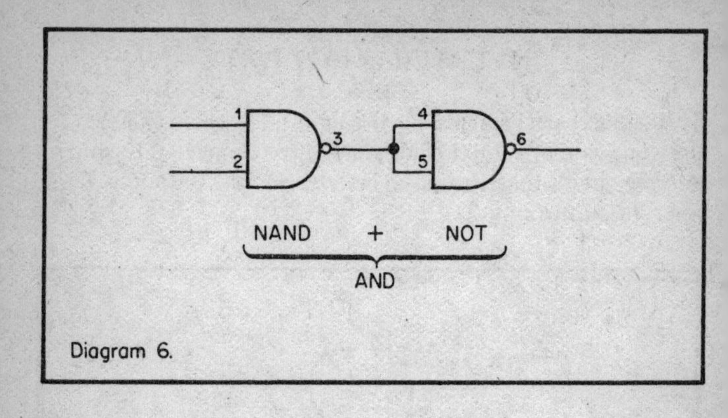

Diagram 6.

Circuit Three
OR GATE

Placing a NOT gate in front of each input to a NAND gate produces an OR gate, see diagram 7. This is a 2-input OR gate.

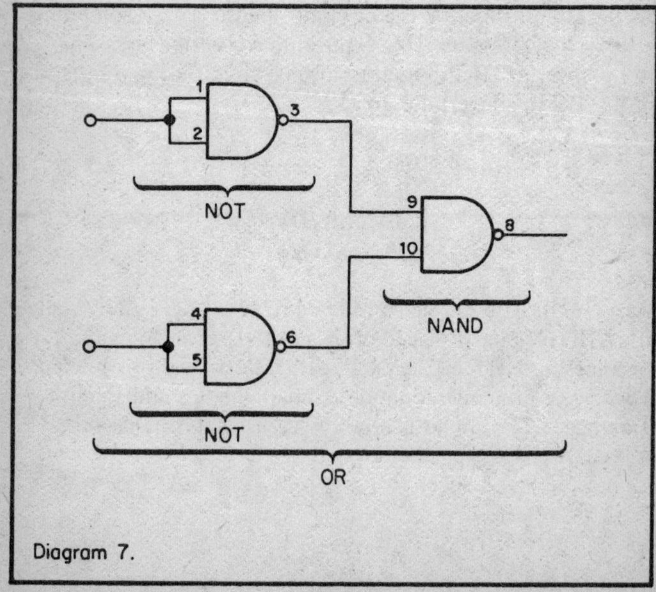

Diagram 7.

Circuit Four
NOR GATE

In circuit (3) an OR gate was formed, a NOR gate is a NOT OR gate, by adding an additional NOT gate after an OR gate an NOR gate is formed (the above is for written use only!) (see diagram 8).

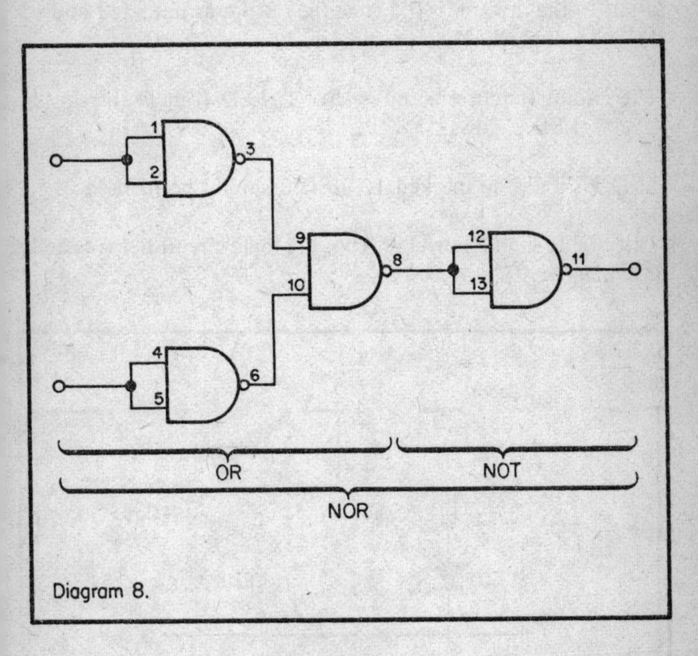

Diagram 8.

Circuit Five
LOGIC LEVEL INDICATOR

This circuit is based on the use of a 7400 NAND gate as an inverter or NOT gate to indicate logic levels. Two red LEDs (light emitting diodes) are used to indicate logic levels – LED 1 and LED 2.

The longer lead of the LED is the cathode in most cases.

If the input is at logic level 1, LED 1 will glow. The output at pin 3 is the inverse of the input, i.e. 0 so LED 2 does not glow.

If the input is at logic level 0, LED 1 does not glow. The input to the inverter is 0, hence the output at pin 3 is 1 and LED 2 will glow.

The circuit function is input level 1, LED 1 glows; input level 0, LED 2 glows.

LED 1 should be marked 1. LED 2 should be marked 0.

The circuit can be powered from the logic circuit being tested (see diagram 9).

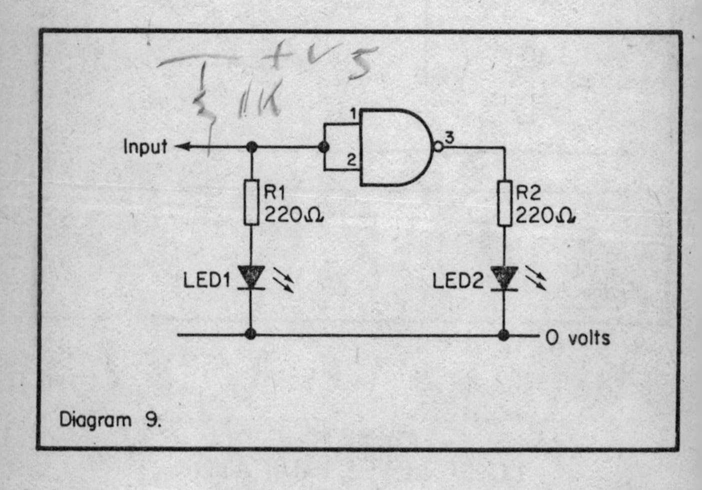

Diagram 9.

Circuit Six
BISTABLE LATCH (S.R. FLIP-FLOP)

This circuit uses two NAND gates cross coupled to form a

bistable latch circuit. The outputs are labelled Q and $\overline{Q}$. The bar over the Q indicates NOT. The two outputs Q and $\overline{Q}$ are the complement of one another, i.e. if Q is at logic level 1, $\overline{Q}$ is 0; if Q is 0, $\overline{Q}$ is 1.

The circuit can be triggered into either of two stable states by a suitable input pulse. In effect this gives the circuit a "memory" and makes it a simple 1 bit (one binary digit) store. The two inputs are labelled S and R, Set and Reset, hence this circuit is also called a S.R.F.F. (Set Reset Flip-Flop).

This circuit is very useful and is employed in several circuits following (see diagram 10).

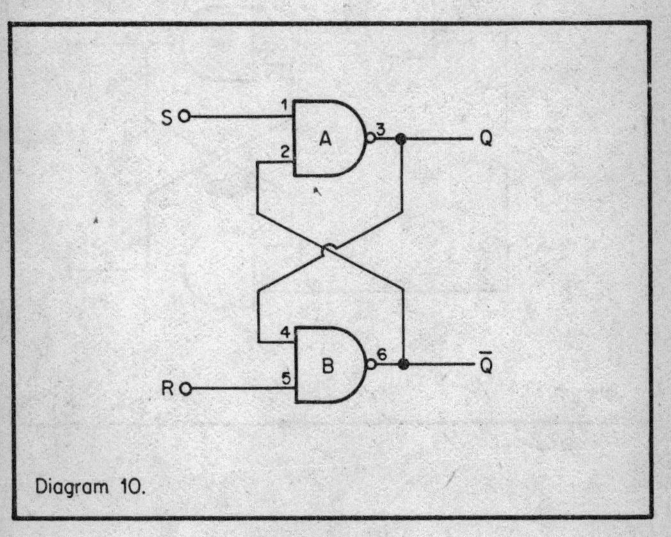

Diagram 10.

Circuit Seven
THE S–R FLIP-FLOP RECTANGULAR WAVE GENERATOR

The SR Flip-Flop circuit can be used as a generator of square waves. If the F.F. is triggered by a sine wave (which could be derived from the mains) of at least 2 volts P.P. the output is a square wave.

The square wave is very square due to the very fast rise and fall times of the circuit (examine output on an oscilloscope).

The inverter or NOT gate fed to the R input results in the inputs to the R and S inputs being complementary (see diagram 11).

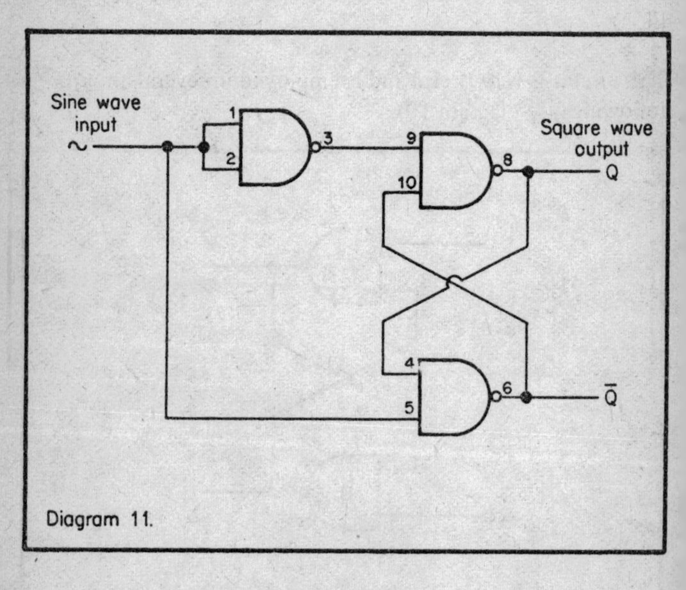

Diagram 11.

Circuit Eight
SWITCH CONTACT BOUNCE ELIMINATOR

This circuit uses a S–R FLIP-FLOP in a contact bounce eliminator. When switch contacts close the initial closure is followed by the contacts jumping rapidly several times between the closed and open position. This phenomenon can generate spurious pulses and cause erratic circuit operation.

In the circuit the first closure of the contacts latches the circuit, contact bounce does not affect the flip-flop. The switch shown is a single pole double throw type (S.P.D.T.) (see diagram 12).

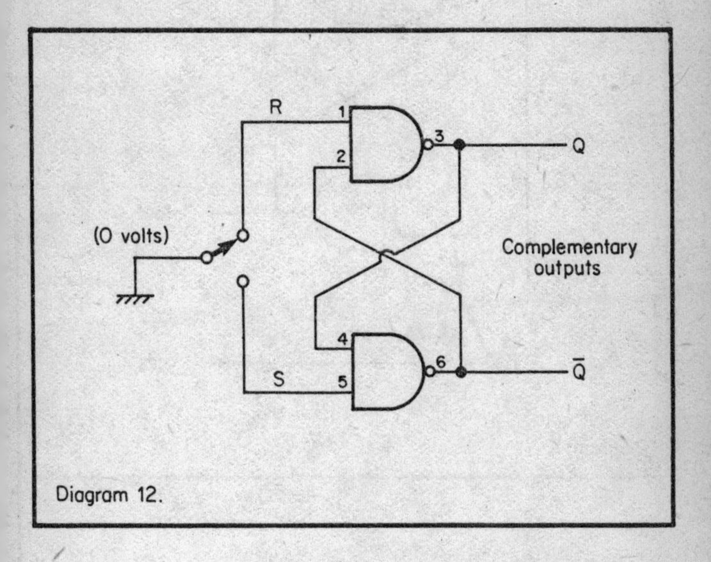

Diagram 12.

Circuit Nine
MANUAL CLOCK

This is a variation on circuit eight. For experimenting with half adder and other logic circuits it is useful to be able to examine the circuit as it functions one pulse at a time. This can be accomplished by the use of a manual clock. Each time the switch is operated a single pulse will appear at the output. The circuit can be used with a binary counter each time the switch is operated one pulse (one only due to the anti-bounce effect of the circuit) will be generated and the count will advance by one (see diagram 13).

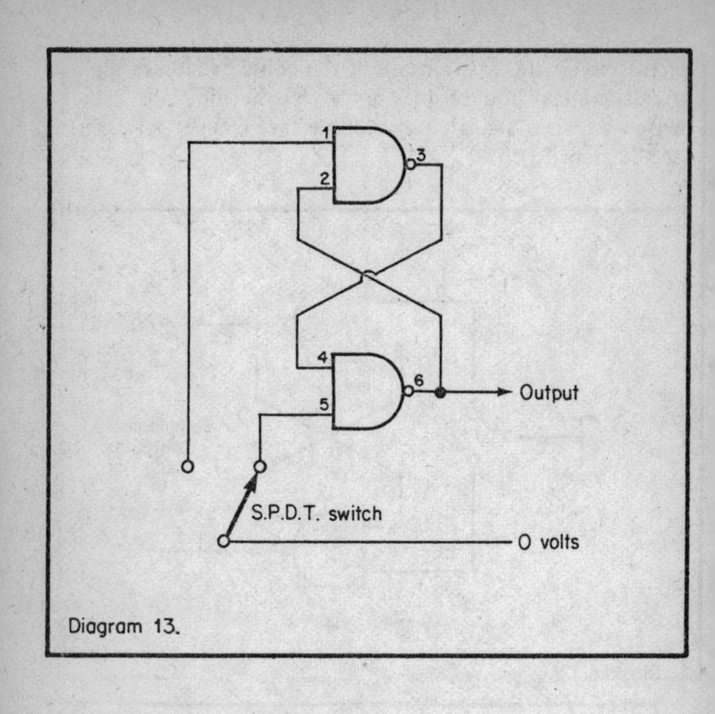

Diagram 13.

Circuit Ten
S–R FLIP-FLOP MEMORY

This circuit is developed from the simple S–R Flip-Flop. The output depends on the previous input. D is the DATA input. An enabling pulse is required to trigger gates B and C. Q is the same logic level as D, i.e. it takes the value of D and remains in this state (see diagram 14).

The lead numbers are not shown to simplify the diagram, all five gates are 2 input NAND, two 7400s are required.

Diagram 14 is a logic circuit only, but is readily translated into a circuit diagram. This simplifies diagrams which have large numbers of logic gates involved. The enable signal can be a pulse from circuit nine.

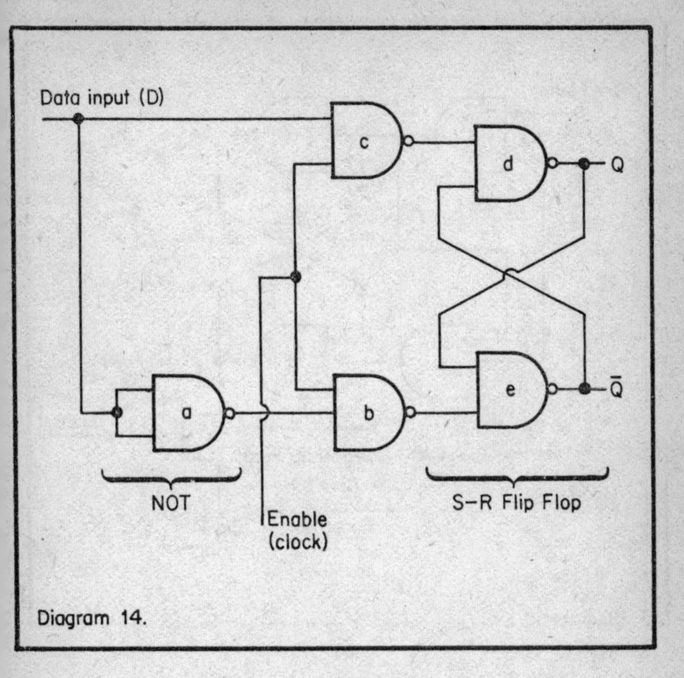

Diagram 14.

The circuit operates in the presence of a "CLOCK" signal, a fundamental principle in computer operation.

Circuits nine and ten can be constructed from two 7400 I.C.s and connected together.

Circuit Eleven
CLOCK CONTROLLED FLIP-FLOP

Circuit eleven is a variation on circuit ten. The date input is controlled by a clock signal, the output from the S–R Flip-Flop is also controlled by the clock.

This Flip-Flop can be used in a storage register. The clock is a master controller of the flow of pulses in and out (see diagram 15).

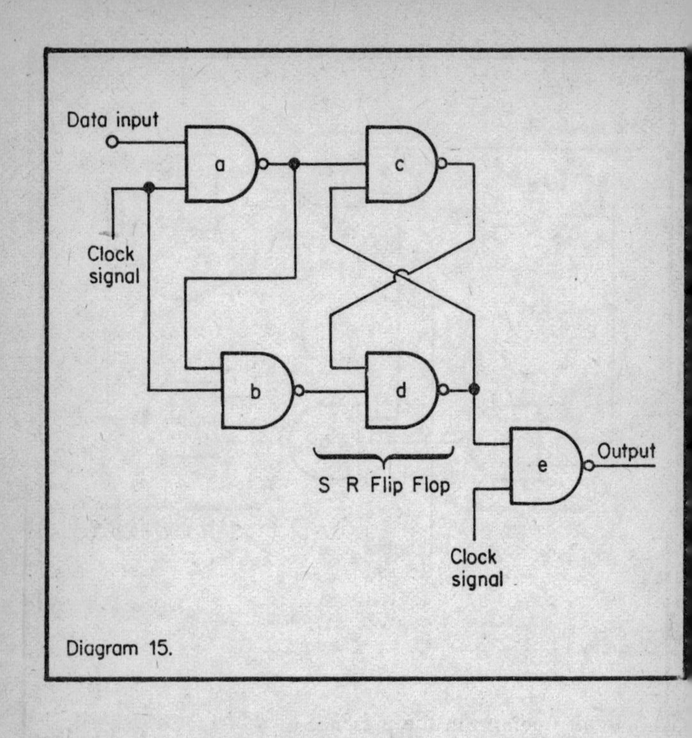

Diagram 15.

Circuit Twelve
HIGH SPEED PULSE INDICATOR AND DETECTOR

This circuit is developed from the S—R Flip-Flop and is used to detect and indicate a single pulse in a logic circuit.

A single pulse latches the circuit, the output is fed to the inverter and the red LED glows. The circuit will remain in this state until it is cleared by operating the S.P.S.T. reset switch. Test with circuit nine (see diagram 16).

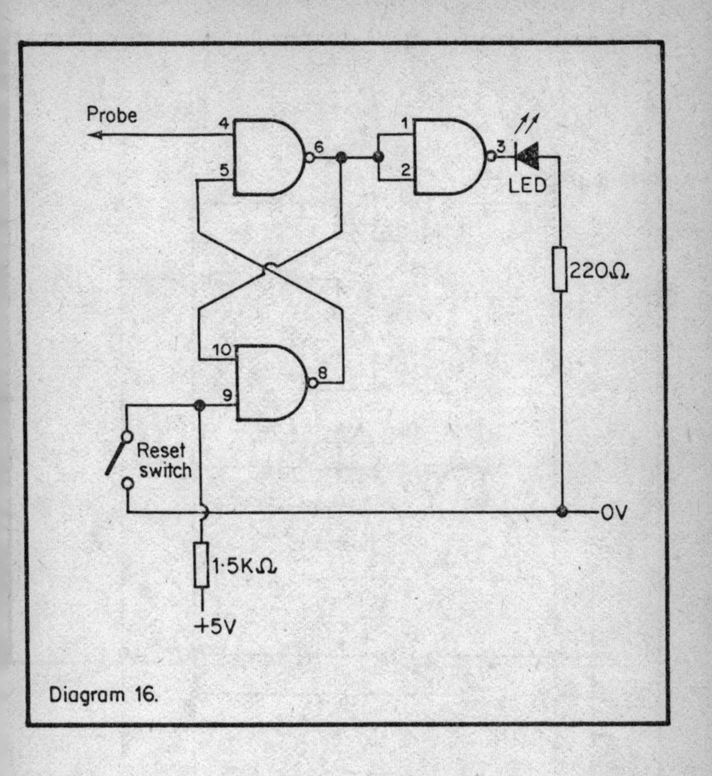

Diagram 16.

Circuit Thirteen
"SNAP!" INDICATOR

This circuit is another use of the S–R Flip-Flop and uses two flip-flops. Seven gates are required. The basic principle in this circuit is the use of S–R flip-flops and INHIBIT lines. S1 and S2 are switches which control the flip-flops. Once a flip-flop has latched the associated LED glows and the other flip-flop is inhibited from latching. If the switches are push button types – releasing the switch resets the circuit. The diodes used are OA91 or any general purpose germanium diode (see diagram 17).

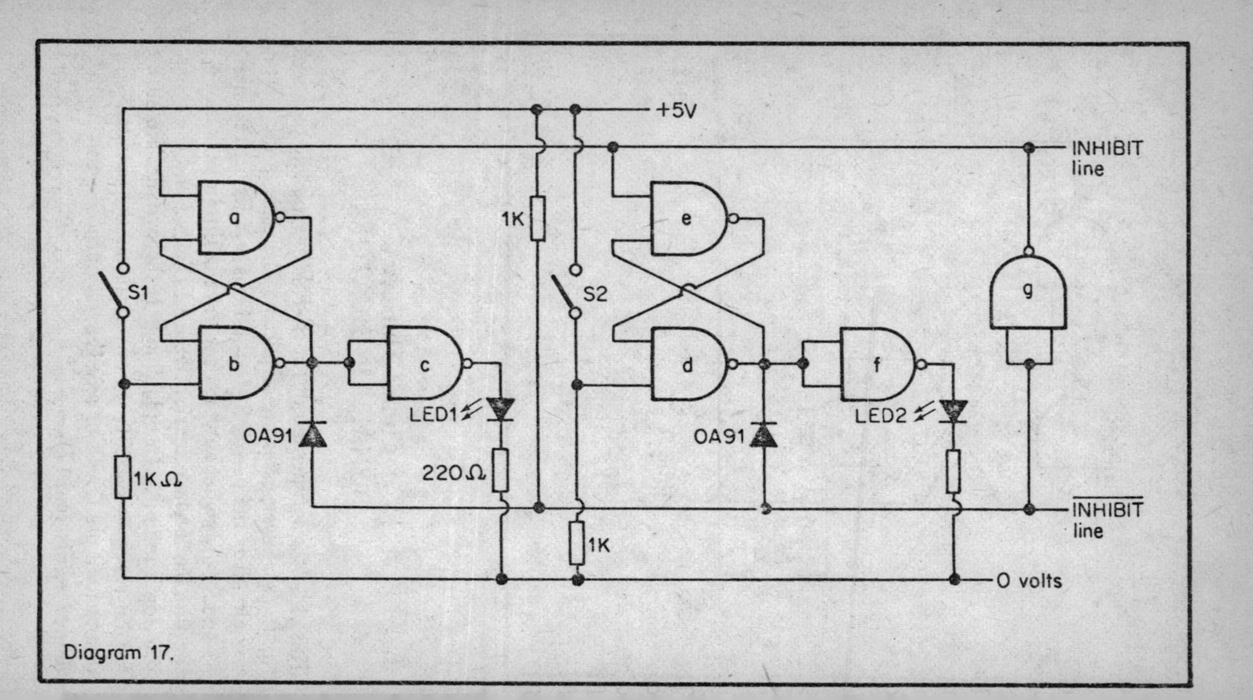
+5V
INHIBIT line
$\overline{\text{INHIBIT}}$ line
0 volts
a
b
c
d
e
f
g
S1
S2
1K
1K
1KΩ
220Ω
LED1
LED2
OA91
OA91

Diagram 17.

Gates A, B, C are the circuit for S1 and LED 1.

Gates D, E, F are the circuits for S2 and LED 2.

Gate G ensures that the INHIBIT and $\overline{\text{INHIBIT}}$ lines are complementary.

Many of the early transistor computers are now being broken up and the logic boards sold at low prices. Many of them used logic gates constructed from germanium diodes, these diodes are ideal for use instead of the OA91.

Circuit Fourteen
LOW FREQUENCY AUDIO OSCILLATOR

The circuit uses two NAND gates connected as inverters and cross coupled to form an astable multivibrator. The frequency can be altered by increasing the value of C1 and C2 (lower frequency) or decreasing the value of C1 and C2 (higher frequency). As electrolytic capacitors are used observe the polarity as shown in the diagram 18.

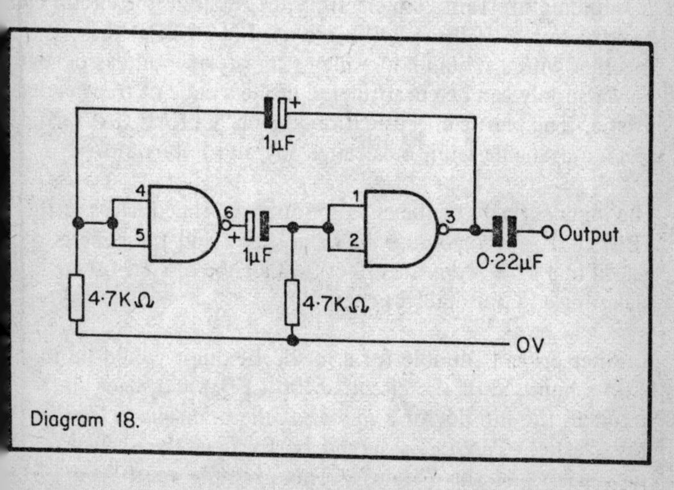

Diagram 18.

Circuits fifteen, sixteen and seventeen are also examples of low frequency oscillators developed from circuit fourteen, but in these the output is used to make LEDs flash. Note the close similarity of the circuits.

If LEDs are connected up in this circuit they will flash but the flashing rate is so high that the eye cannot distinguish the individual flashes. This principle is used in pocket calculators.

Circuit Fifteen
TWIN LED FLASHER

This circuit uses two NAND gates to form a very low frequency oscillator, this drives two red LEDs and causes them to flash alternately. The circuit uses two NAND gates, the other two gates in a 7400 can also be used in a similar circuit but with different value capacitors to produce a different flashing rate. If higher value electrolytic capacitors are used the LEDs will flash at a slower rate. Two suggested "novelty" projects using this circuit, are as follows.

If subminiature Tantalum electrolytics are used, the circuit can be very small. If three 7400s are used (12 LEDs) these together with a subminiature mains transformer and associated power supply can be encapsulated inside a cube of transparent plastic. The plastic encapsulation kits or "CLEAR CASTING" kits are available from most large toy and hobby stores.

The inner surfaces of the cube produce multiple images of the LEDs, if 12 red or orange LEDs are used and the cube is placed in a dark room the effect is of a cube of cold fire or flickering and pulsing light energy.

Another project suitable for a medical exhibit would be to build a hundred of the circuits (400 LEDs) and place the circuit in the interior of a model of the brain made from grey plastic. The LEDs should be fixed in the surface convolutions of the "brain". This example apart from electronics could be titled "THOUGHT".

Another idea is to place the circuit behind a painting or picture of a war scene, battle at sea, aircraft or tank battle. Place the red or orange LEDs in the guns to simulate firing (see diagram 19).

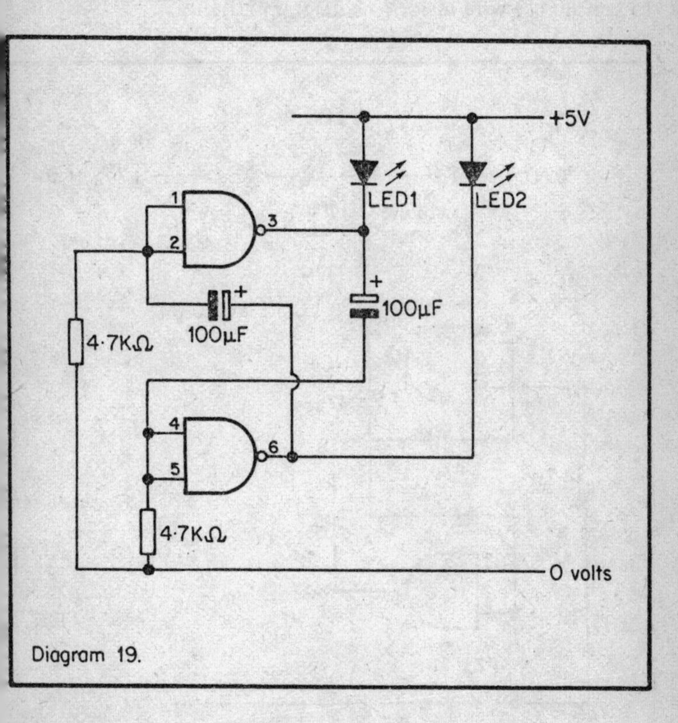

Diagram 19.

Circuit Sixteen
FUSE TESTER

A simple development from circuit fifteen is a fuse tester working from a 7½-volt or 9-volt battery. LED1 indicates that the circuit is working. A green LED is best for this (and it also reduces the voltage applied to the I.C.).

LED1 indicates the circuit is operational when the TEST button is pressed. If LED2, a red LED, flashes this shows that the fuse is intact, if the fuse has blown, i.e. open circuit, the LED2 does not flash. This is a useful circuit because many fuses (e.g. the 1" types used on mains plugs) are made from a ceramic tube and it is not possible to see the use wire inside (see diagram 20).

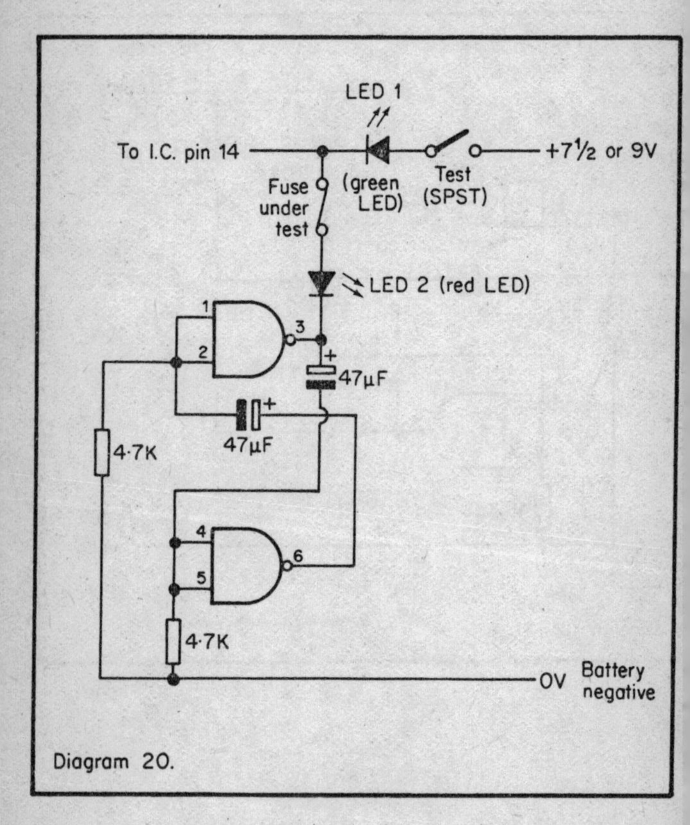

Diagram 20.

Circuit Seventeen
STROBOSCOPE

This circuit is developed from circuit fifteen and is a low power stroboscope. The circuit is really a high speed LED flasher. The red LED flashes but the eye is unable to resolve the individual flashes (persistence of vision).

The output is not very great so the stroboscope should be used in a darkened room. The gauged variable resistors alter the frequency of the flash so that the stroboscope can be used to give a stationary display. The resistors are described as 10 K Ω + 10 KΩ gauged variable LIN (i.e. LINEAR TAPER), or 10 KΩ + 10 KΩ stereo pot(entiometer) – LIN (see diagram 21).

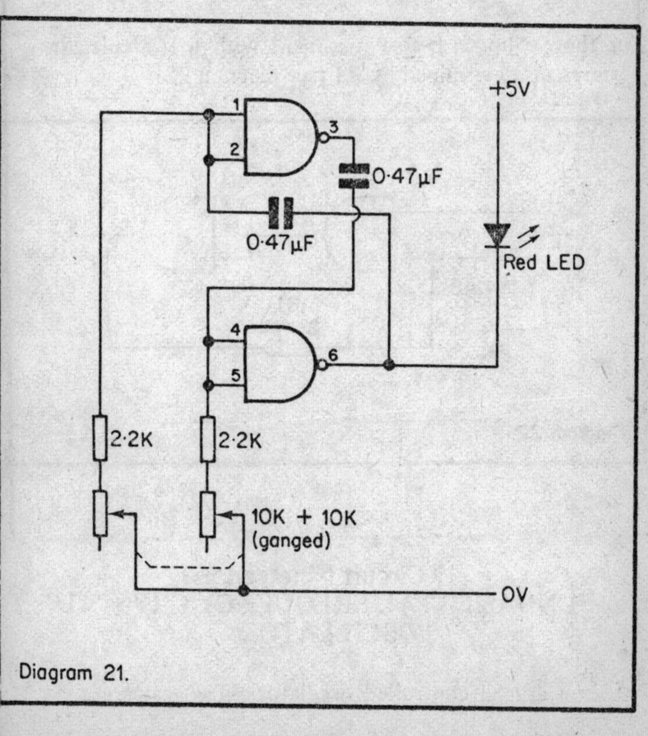

Diagram 21.

The stroboscope can be used at a much higher frequency by changing the value of the timing capacitor. The LED is a light emitting diode and being a diode will work at a very high frequency. I suggest that it might be possible to take very high speed photographs using a LED strobe. If anyone does wish to attempt this note that high speed infra-red sensitive film could be used with an infra-red emitting diode.

Circuit Eighteen
LOW HYSTERESIS SCHMITT TRIGGER

Two NAND gates function as a Schmitt trigger in this circuit. The diode is a high speed silicon type 1N4148 or 1N914.

For those who wish to experiment with the circuit, the hysteresis is determined by R1 (see diagram 22).

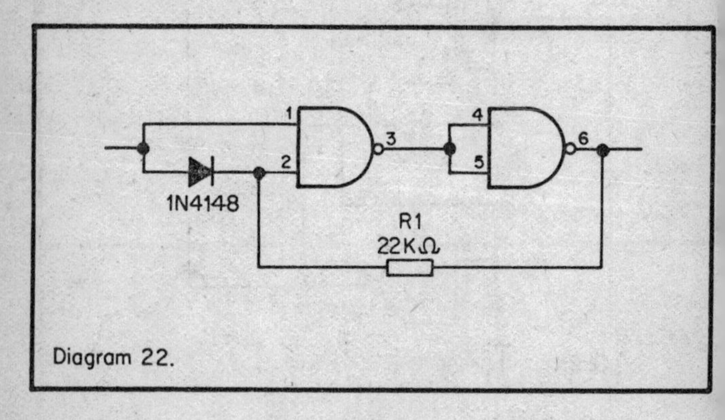

Diagram 22.

Circuit Nineteen
FUNDAMENTAL FREQUENCY CRYSTAL OSCILLATOR

This is a crystal controlled oscillator. Two gates are

connected as inverters, the resistors bias the gates into the correct operating point. The third gate is connected as a "buffer" to avoid loading the oscillator.

Note that when a crystal is used in this circuit, it will oscillate at its fundamental frequency, i.e. NOT at a harmonic or overtone frequency. If the circuit works at a frequency much lower than expected, this means that the crystal frequency marked is an overtone, i.e. a multiple of the fundamental frequency (see diagram 23).

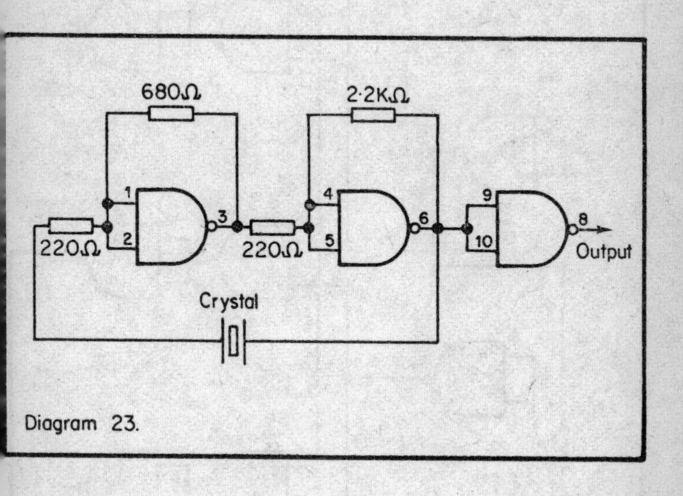

Diagram 23.

Circuit Twenty
TWO BIT DECODER

This is a simple two bit decoder. The inputs are along lines A and B, outputs are along lines 0, 1, 2, 3.

A can be 0 or 1.
B can be 0 or 1.

If A and B are at 1, this is a binary count of 11 equal to

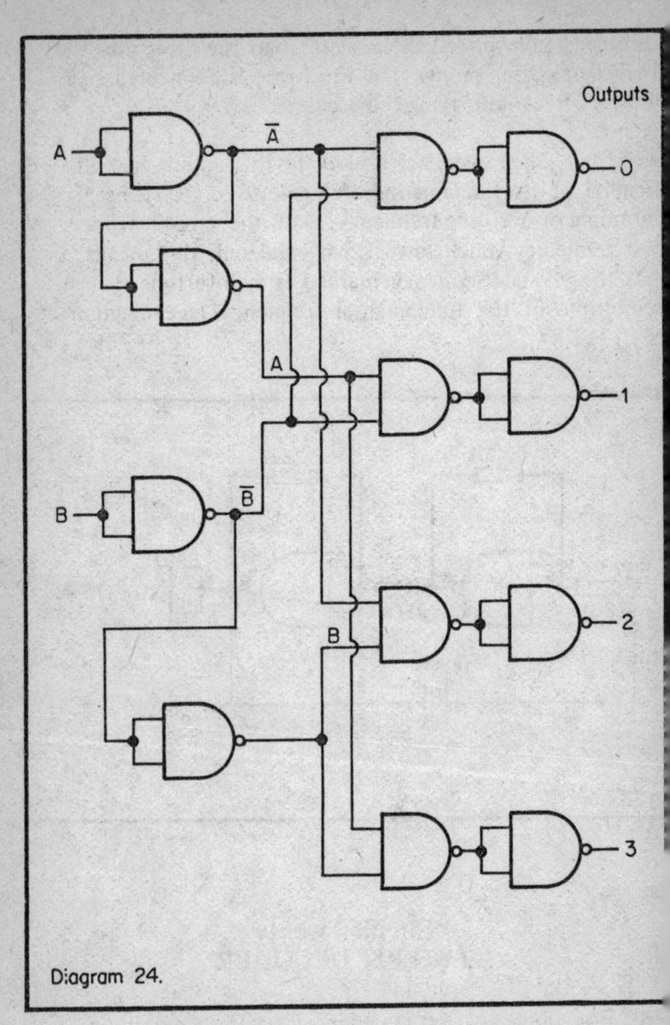

Diagram 24.

denary 3 and the output along line 3 is "high". Similarly, A, 0 B, 0 output line 0. Maximum count depends on the number of inputs, maximum counter with two inputs is $2^2 - 1 = 3$. The circuit can be expanded, e.g. if four inputs are used A, B, C and D, maximum count is $2^4 - 1 = 15$ and the outputs are from 0 to 15.

Note on the circuit the use of NOT gates. Some lines are B, some $\overline{B}$ (not B), note the inversion of B to $\overline{B}$ and later inversion of $\overline{B}$ back to B on some lines.

This is a simple circuit but it requires 3 x 7400 I.C.s (12 gates) and the interconnections are becoming complicated. The transistor and I.C. produced revolutions in electronics, but it may not be appreciated that a development of almost equal importance was the printed circuit. The interconnections on a printed circuit may be very difficult to work out for the "Master" board design, but once this has been tested and proved the circuit board, containing all the connections, can be reproduced photographically thousands or millions of times (see diagram 24).

Circuit Twenty-One
TWO BIT DECODER (SIMPLIFIED)

The two bit decoder of circuit twenty required 12 gates, three 7400 I.C.s. It can be seen that the circuit simplifies to four NOT gates and four AND gates. A simpler version can be used by employing the special purpose inverter and AND gate I.C.s.

The 7404 contains six NOT gates or inverters and the 7408 contains four 2-input AND gates. By using a 7404 and 7408 only two I.C.s are required and two gates of the 7404 are spare.

On the 7404 and 7408 pins 7 are 0 volt and pins 14 + 5V (as with the 7400) (see diagram 25).

Circuit Twenty-Two
PHOTO SENSITIVE LATCHING CIRCUIT

This is a simple photoelectric circuit using two NAND gates

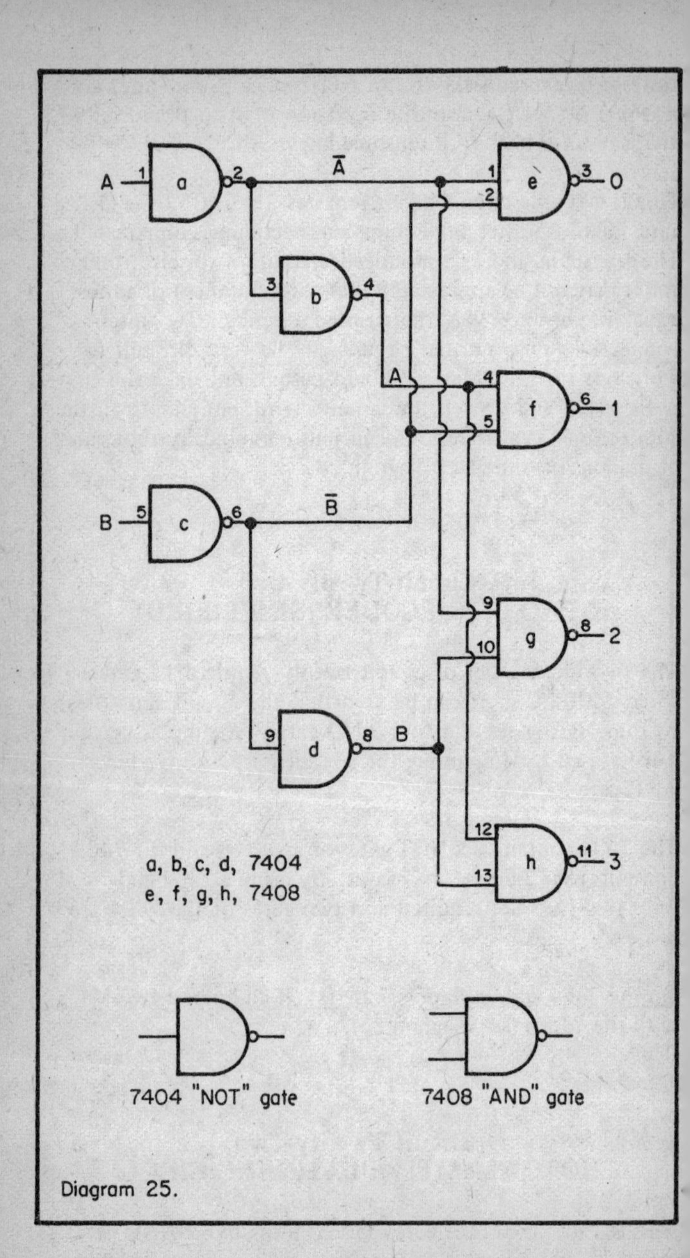
A
1
a
2
Ā
1
2
e
3
0
3
b
4
A
4
5
f
6
1
B
5
c
6
B̄
9
10
g
8
2
9
d
8
B
12
13
h
11
3
a, b, c, d, 7404
e, f, g, h, 7408
7404 "NOT" gate
7408 "AND" gate
Diagram 25.

to form a circuit with latching action. The transistor used is a general purpose audio NPN silicon type such as the BC108, the lead connections are shown on diagram 26. The photo sensitive element is a Cds (Cadmium Sulphide) photo-conductive cell. The CdS cell is in effect a resistor whose resistance varies in accordance with the light shining on it. In complete darkness the resistance may be 10MΩ (10 million Ohms) and in comparison directly under a bright electric light the resistance may drop to 100Ω.

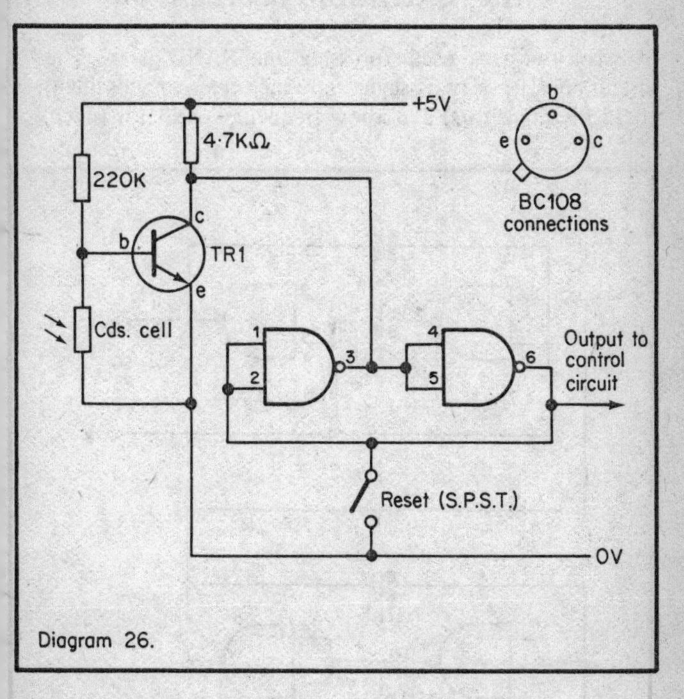

Diagram 26.

The circuit operation is as follows. The Cds cell is normally illuminated by a small torch bulb, and the resistance of the cell will be very low, grounding the base of TR1. As the base is grounded Tr1 does not conduct hence there is no voltage drop across the 4.7 KΩ resistor in the collector circuit, so that the voltage at the collector is high. If the light is blocked off the resistance of the Cds cell rises (not instantaneously – there is a slight delay in the resistance change of a Cds cell – not important in this circuit). Tr1 conducts, there is a voltage drop across the 4.7 KΩ resistor and the voltage at the collector falls. This fall in voltage triggers the latch. The latch has to be reset by momentarily depressing the switch.

Circuit Twenty-Three
TWIN TONE AUDIO OSCILLATOR

This is a two tone oscillator using four NAND gates. The circuit consists of two oscillators, a high frequency oscillator (0.22 μF capacitors) and a low frequency oscillator (47 μF

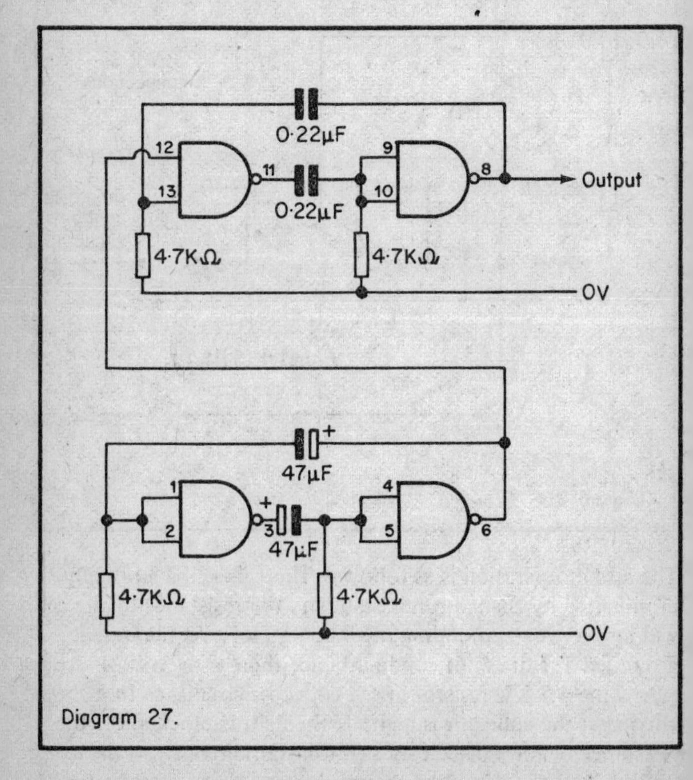

Diagram 27.

capacitors). The oscillators are connected together in such a way that the high frequency is modulated by the low frequency. The circuit gives a warbling output which is much pleasanter than the single tone produced by a 2-gate oscillator (see diagram 27).

Circuit Twenty-Four
CRYSTAL CLOCK OSCILLATOR

This is a crystal oscillator for use with a L.S.I. I.C. clock "chip" and provides a 50 Hz reference when used with an I.C. frequency divider chain.

The output is at 500 kHz and should be connected to four 7490 I.C.s in cascade. Each 7490 divides by 10 giving a total division of 10,000, the output is then 50 Hz (500,000 ÷ 10 ÷ 10 ÷ 10 ÷ 10 = 50).

The 50 Hz reference is usually derived from the mains but a clock I.C. can be inaccurate if the mains is unstable due to

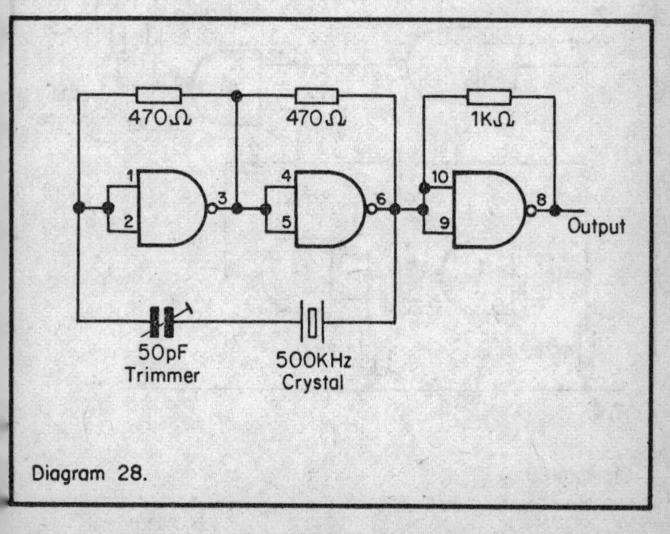

Diagram 28.

waveform distortion which can occur if thyristor equipment is used on the same phase of the mains (next door for example).

Drill controllers, power controllers, light dimmers and some colour televisions use thyristor circuits which can disturb the mains. If you have an electronic clock which behaves erratically, this is the most probable cause.

The 50 pF trimmer is adjusted so that the crystal frequency is exactly 500 kHz (see diagram 28).

Circuit Twenty-Five
SWITCHED OSCILLATOR

This circuit consists of a tone generator and an electronic

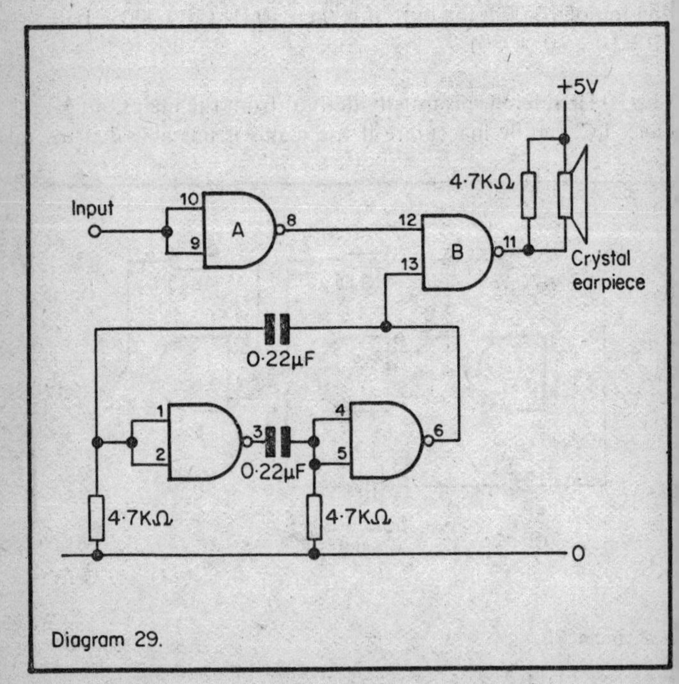

Diagram 29.

switch. The tone generator runs continuously but there is no output from the earpiece until there is a logic 0 input to gate A. A logic 0 input at gate A is inverted to a logic 1. The logic 1 opens gate B and the audio tone is fed to the earpiece. Although a small crystal earpiece is used this produces quite a loud sound. The circuit could be used as a buzzar with an electronic alarm clock I.C. (see diagram 29).

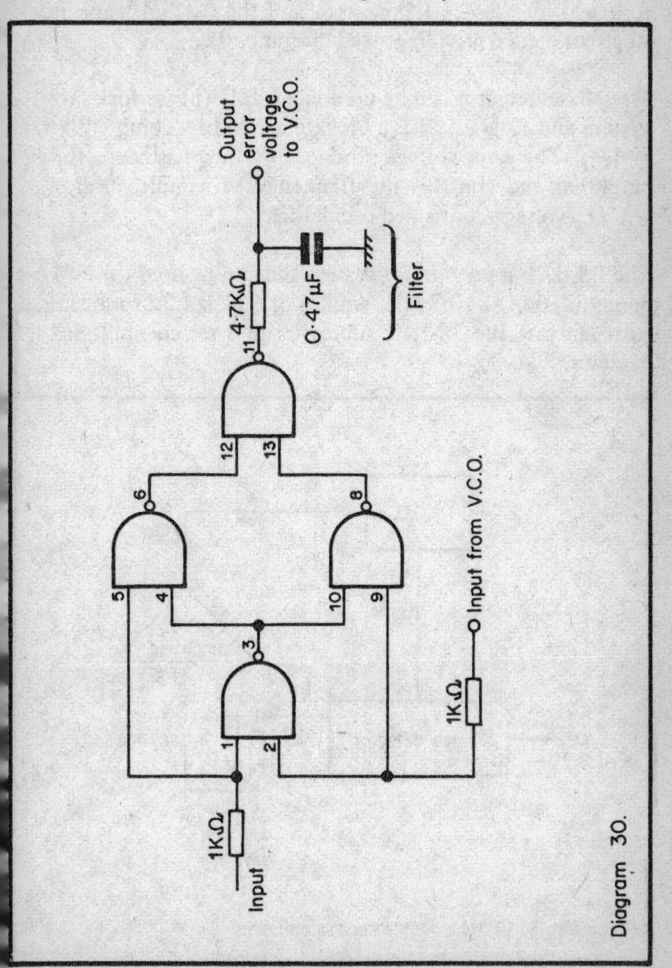

Diagram 30.

Circuit Twenty-Six
PHASE DETECTOR

This is a phase detector which uses four NAND gates. The phase detector compares two inputs and produces an error voltage in proportion to the difference between the two frequencies used as inputs. The output from the detector is followed by the 4.7 KΩ resistor and the 0.47 μF capacitor to give a d.c. error voltage (see diagram 30).

The phase detector can be used in a P.L.L. (phase lock loop) system and diagram 31 is a block diagram of a complete P.L.L. system. The error voltage produced by the phase detector is amplified and controls the frequency of a multivibrator V.C.O. (voltage controlled oscillator).

The P.L.L. is a very useful system and can be used for F.M demodulation at 10.7 MHz (radio) or 6 MHz (TV sound) or to regenerate the 38 KHz subcarrier in a stereo multiplex decoder.

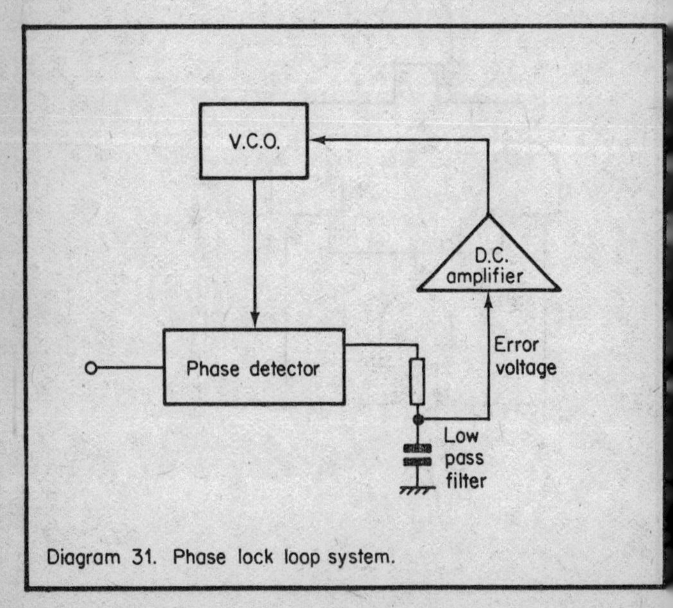

Diagram 31. Phase lock loop system.

Circuit Twenty-Seven
RF ATTENUATOR

This circuit uses four gates to form a "chopper' which

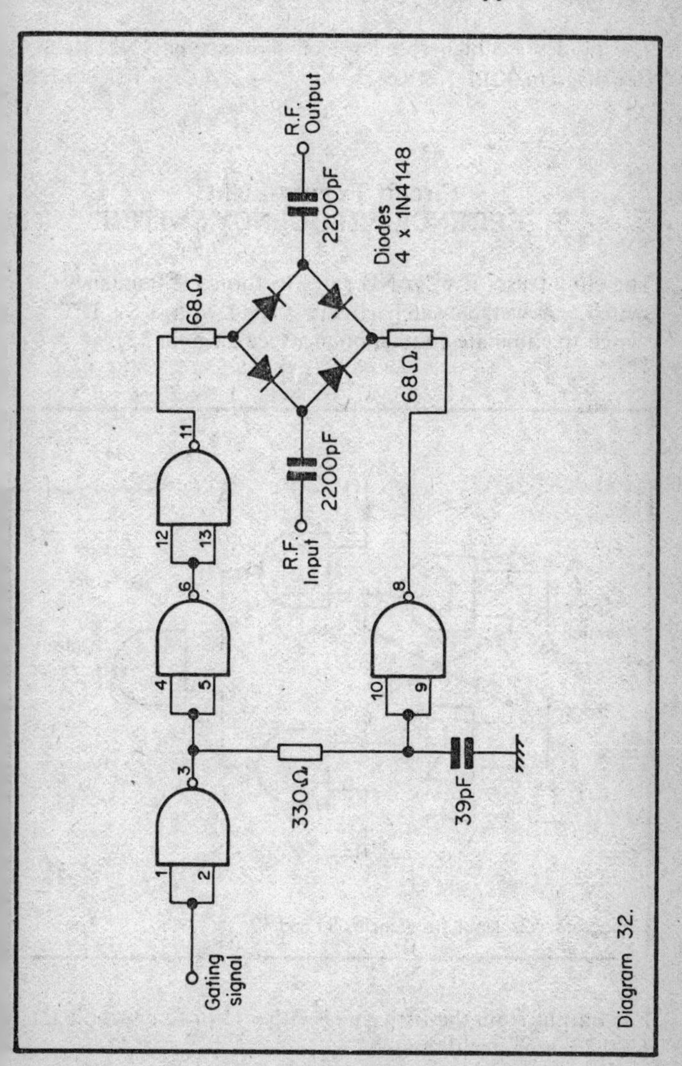

Diagram 32.

controls the diode bridge. The diode bridge conducts to allow the passage of RF or does not conduct to block the passage of RF. The amount of RF allowed through is a function of the gating signal.

The diodes are high speed silicon diodes type 1N4148 (see diagram 32).

Circuit Twenty-Eight
REFERENCE FREQUENCY SWITCH

The circuit uses five NAND gates to form a 2-frequency switch. A bistable latch circuit is used with a S.P.D.T. switch to eliminate contact bounce (see diagram 33).

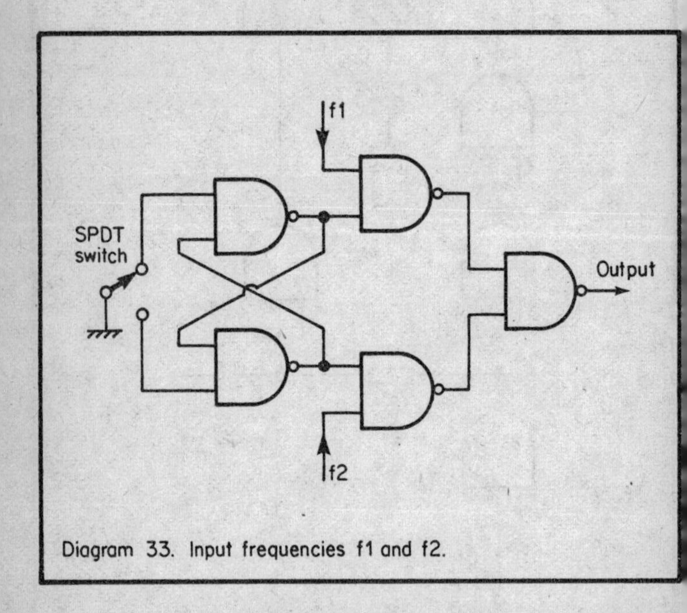

Diagram 33. Input frequencies f1 and f2.

The output from the fifth gate is either f1 or f2 depending on the switch position used.

Circuit Twenty-Nine
SWITCH CONTACT BOUNCE ELIMINATOR

Most switches especially low cost types display some degree of "contact bounce". This is of no consequence in most electronic circuits, but if such a switch is used in a logic circuit, operation of the switch may produce spurious pulses.

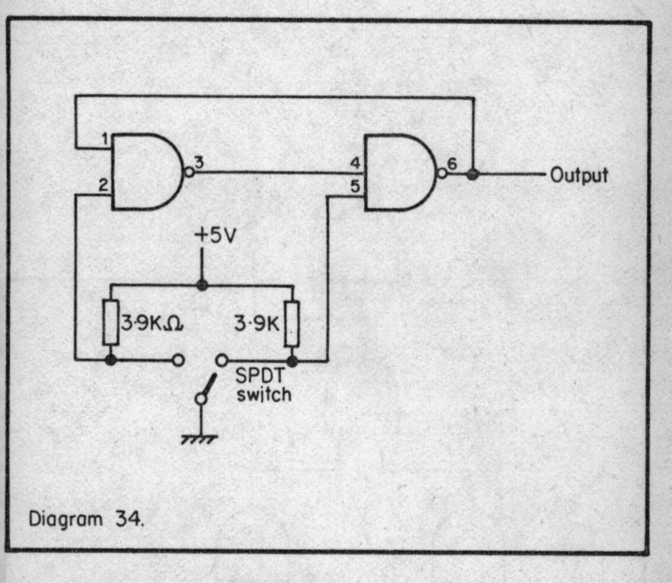

Diagram 34.

The circuit uses two NAND gates (see diagram 34). This application can also be used as a single pulse generator for use with testing or demonstrating flip-flops or other logic circuits.

Circuit Thirty
TWO BIT DATA CHECK

This is another simple "computer type" circuit which can be used to demonstrate logic functions. Spurious pulses can occur in a computer causing errors. Error checking is done by adding an extra bit (binary digit) in "words" so that the total number of 1s in a computer "word" is always odd or always even.

This system is described as a "PARITY CHECK". The circuit checks odd or even parity for two bits. Note the similarity to the phase detector circuit. This demonstrates how other

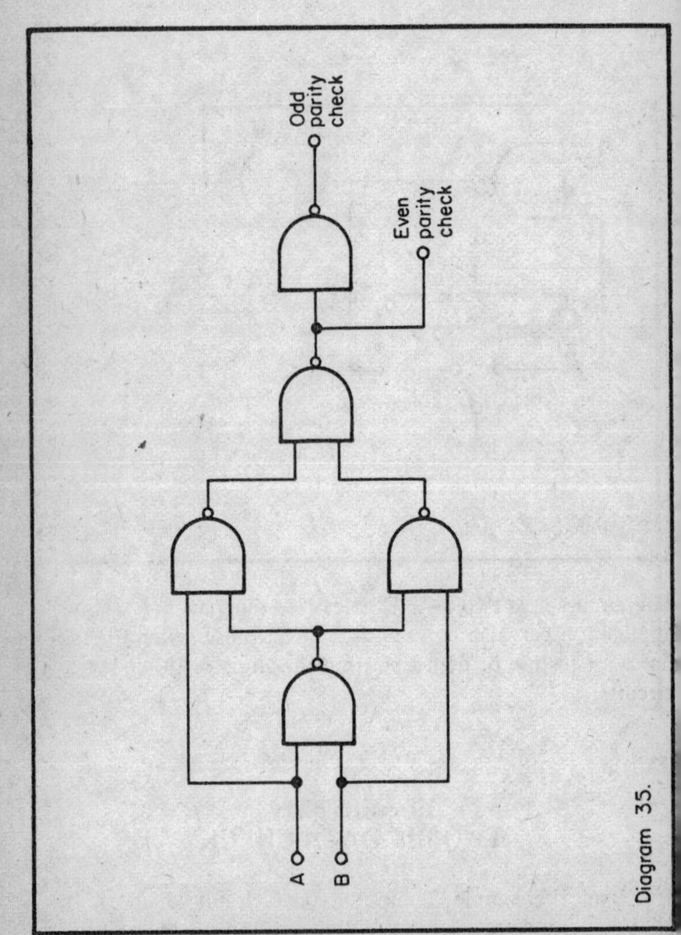

Diagram 35.

applications can be devised by slightly altering the function of a "computer-type" circuit (see diagram 35).

Circuit Thirty-One
BINARY HALF ADDER CIRCUIT

This circuit uses seven NAND gates to form a half adder circuit (see diagram 36).

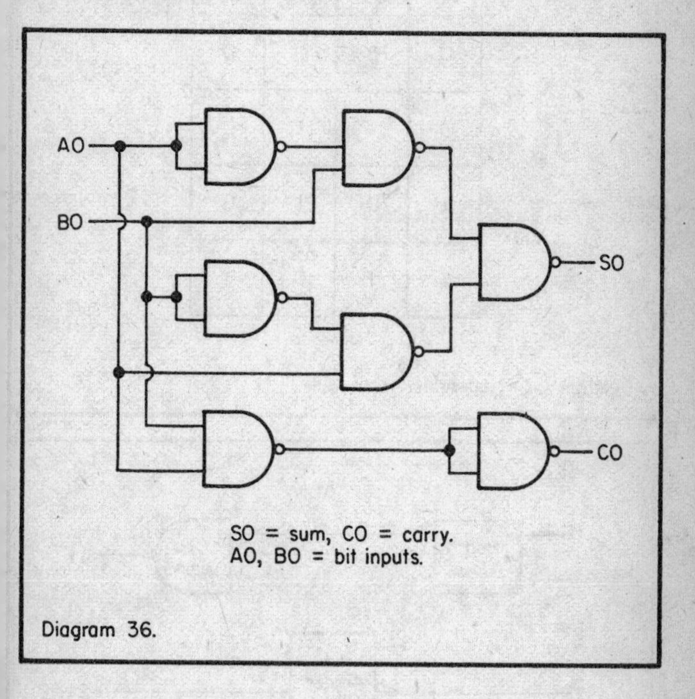

Diagram 36.

A0, B0 are the binary digit inputs. S0, C0 are the sum and carry lines.

In order to understand how these circuits work think how simple arithmetic is taught to children. Refer to the half adder TRUTH Table – diagram 37.

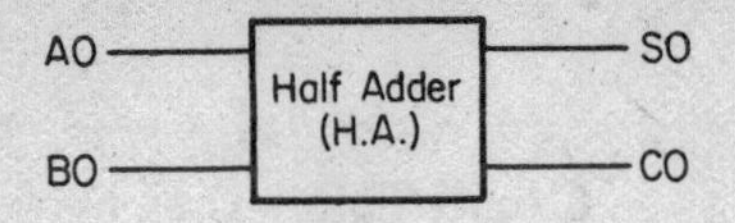

H.A. block diagram.

A0	B0	S0	C0
0	0	0	0
0	1	1	0
1	0	1	0
1	1	0	1

Diagram 37. Half Adder truth table.

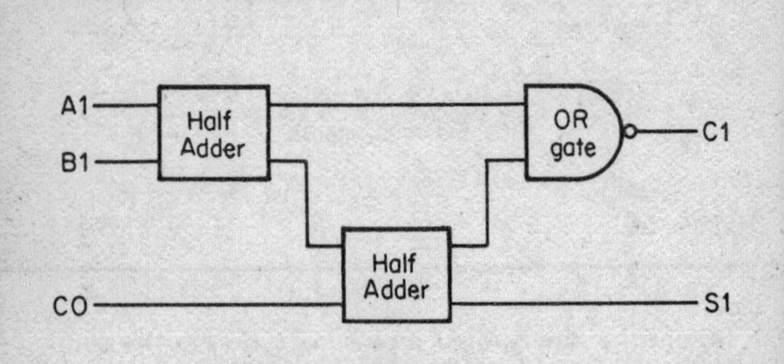

A1 B1 bits input.
C0 carry from previous stage.
S1 is sum, C1 carry to next stage.

Diagram 38. Full adder block diagram.

Consider the Truth Table in terms of binary arithmetic:

0 and 0 is 0
1 and 0 is 1 sum 1 carry 0.
0 and 1 is 1 sum 1 carry 0.
1 and 1 is 10 sum 0 carry 1.

10 is *not* "ten" but is pronounced as "one zero" and represents $1 \times 2^1 + (0 \times 2^0)$.

Two complete half adder circuits plus an "OR" gate form a full adder circuit – see diagram 38.

On diagram 38, A1 and B1 are the binary digits, C0 is the carry from the previous stage, S1 is the sum, C1 is the carry to the next stage.

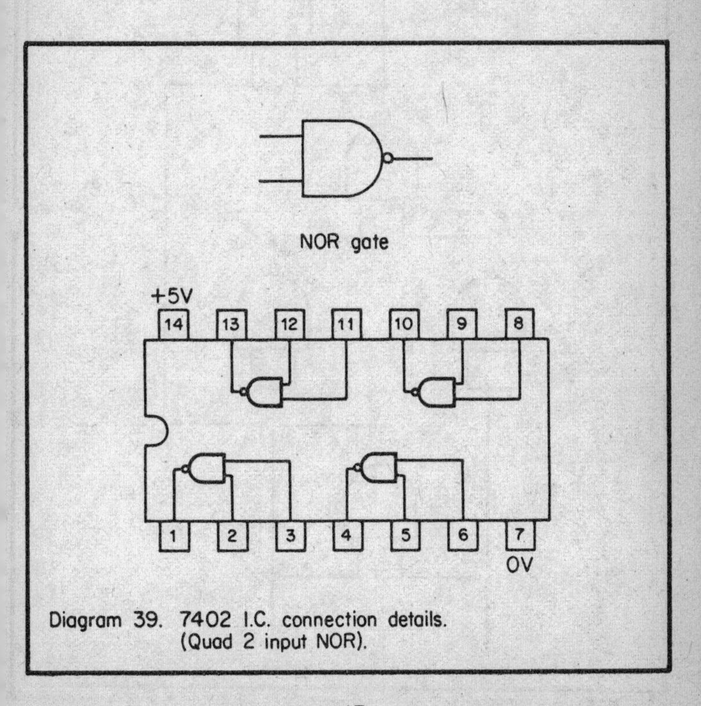

Diagram 39. 7402 I.C. connection details. (Quad 2 input NOR).

Circuit Thirty-Two
NOR GATE HALF ADDER

This circuit and circuit thirty-three are based on the use of NOR gates. The 7402 I.C. contains four 2-input NOR gates.

See diagram 39 for connection details of 7402: pin 7 = 0V; pin 14 = +5V as with the 7400 I.C.

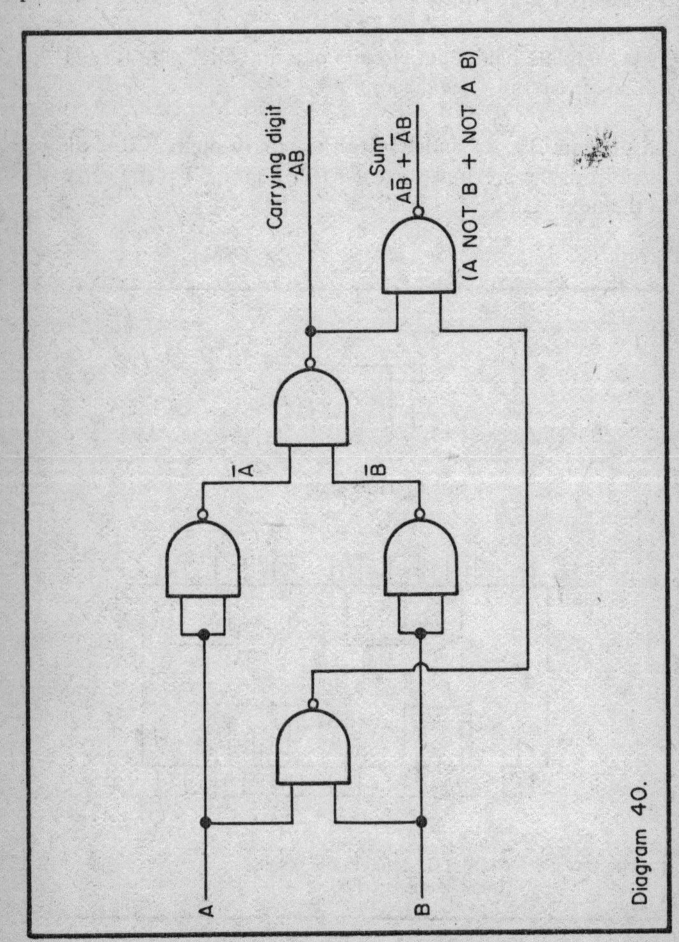

Diagram 40.

The half adder uses five NOR gates – see diagram 40.

Compare circuit thirty-two with circuit thirty-one which uses seven NAND gates. Output lines:

$$\text{sum} = \overline{A}B + A\overline{B} \text{ (NOTA.B + A.NOTB)}$$

$$\text{carry} = A.B$$

Circuit Thirty-Three
NOR GATE FULL ADDER

This is a full adder circuit which uses two NOR gate half adders plus two additional NOR gates.

The circuit uses a total of twelve NOR gates and will require three 7402 I.C.s (see diagram 41).

The output lines are:

$$AB + K(A\overline{B} + \overline{A}B) = \text{(sum)}$$

and

$$\overline{(A\overline{B} + \overline{A}B)K + (A\overline{B} + \overline{A}B)K} = \text{(carry)}.$$

Input lines A, B and K.

K is the carrying digit from the previous column.

Note that the output is via two NOR gates which are equivalent to an OR gate. The circuit resolves again to two half adders plus an OR gate. Compare with previous circuits.

Circuit Thirty-Four
SIMPLE SIGNAL INJECTOR

A simple signal injector for checking the output stages of

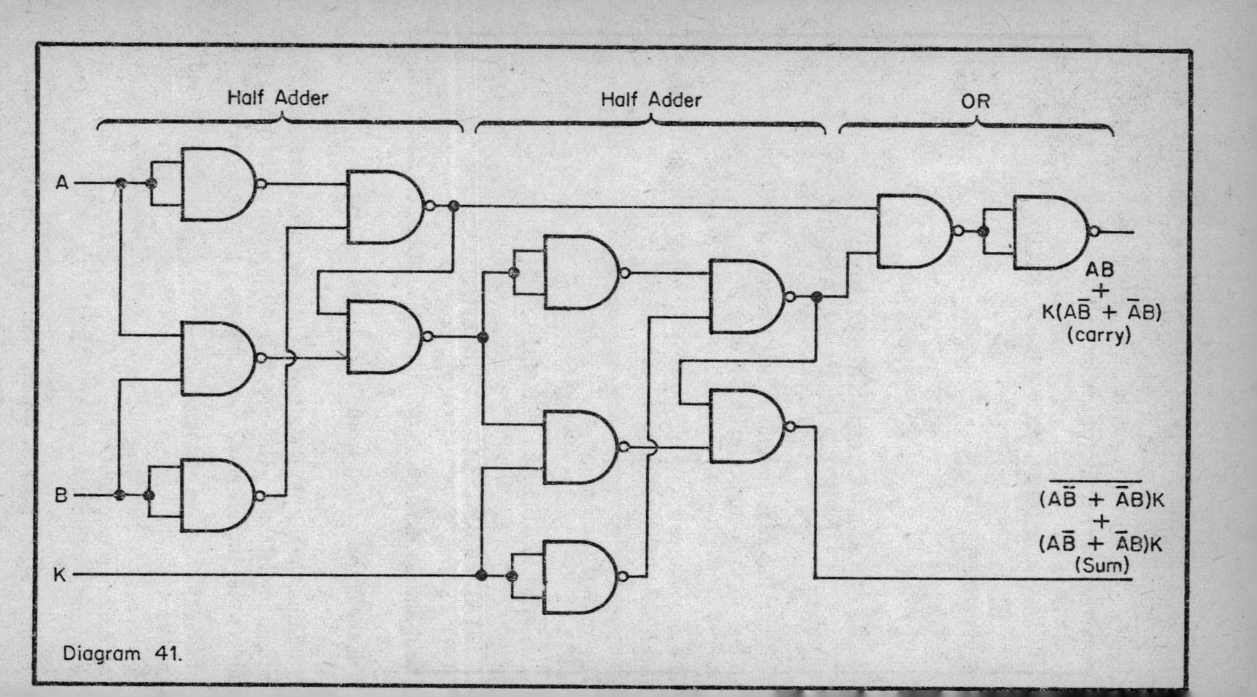

Half Adder
Half Adder
OR
A
B
K
AB
+
$K(A\bar{B} + \bar{A}B)$
(carry)
$\overline{(A\bar{B} + \bar{A}B)K}$
+
$(A\bar{B} + \bar{A}B)K$
(Sum)

Diagram 41.

transistor radios etc. can be made using two NAND gates. The circuit can be powered by three 1½ volt batteries in series (see diagram 42).

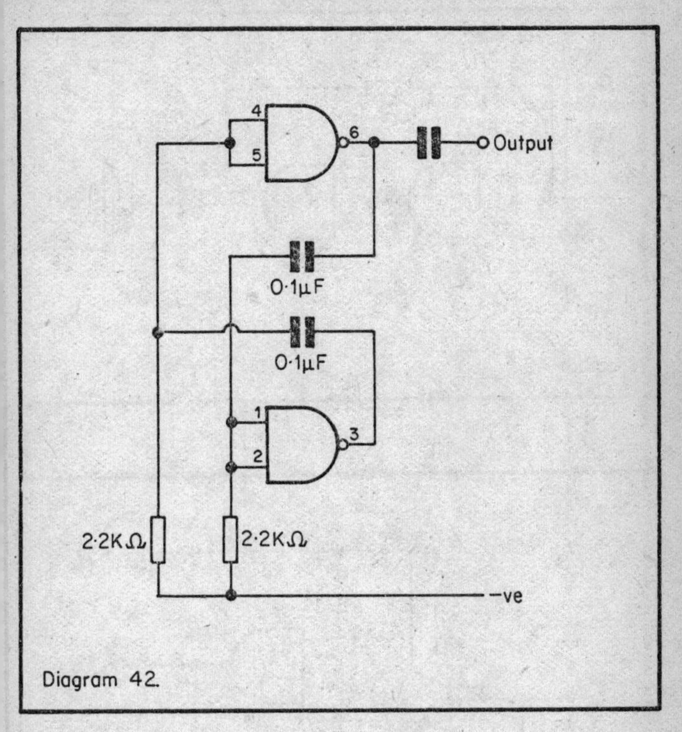

Diagram 42.

Circuit Thirty-Five
SIMPLE AMPLIFIER

Two NAND gates connected as inverters can be connected in series to form a simple audio amplifier. The 4.7 KΩ resistor produces negative feedback in the circuit, but the distortion is still high. The amplifier will drive a 25 to 80 ohm impedance loudspeaker directly. An 8Ω loudspeaker can be connected but the I.C. may get very warm in use due to the extra power dissipated.

A lower value of resistor, e.g. 2.2 KΩ can be used for better results, but lower volume (see diagram 43).

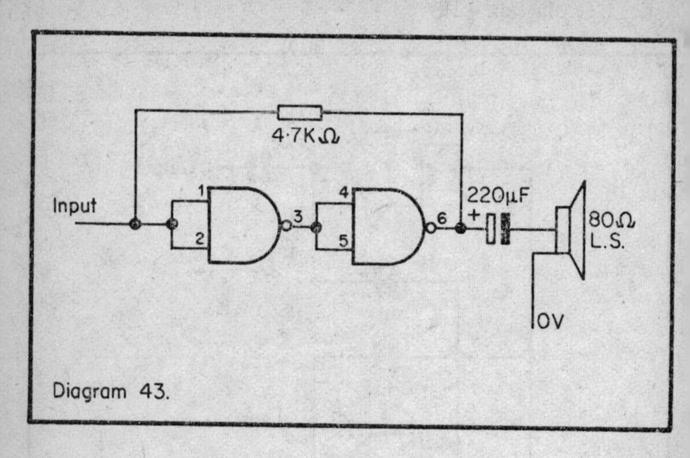

Diagram 43.

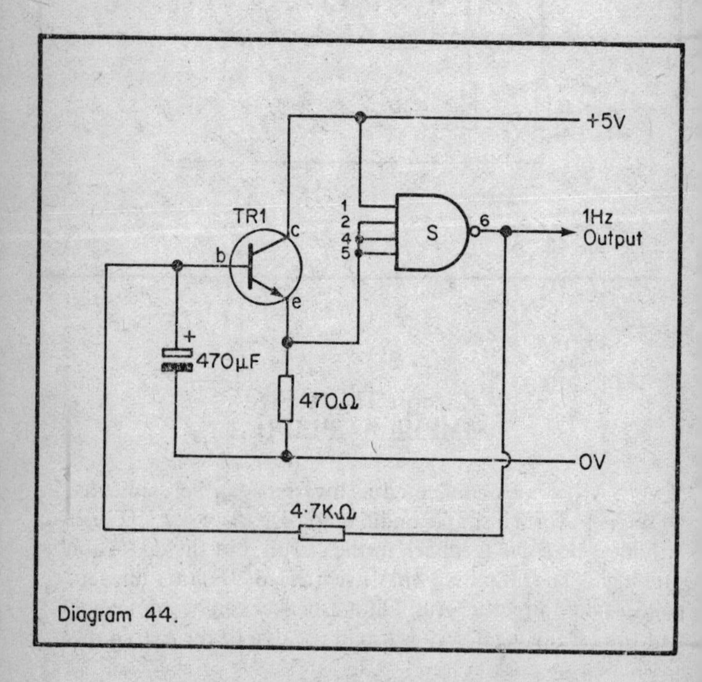

Diagram 44.

Circuit Thirty-Six
LOW SPEED CLOCK

his circuit uses a Schmitt trigger in a low frequency oscil-
tor when the RC values are as shown. The clock frequency
about 1 Hz, i.e. 1 pulse per second. The low speed clock
useful for demonstrating the action of circuits "in slow
otion". TR1 is a general purpose NPN transistor such as the
C108 (see diagram 44).

413 pin 7 = 0V. Pin 14 + 5V.

he 7413 is a dual Schmitt trigger. The corresponding pins
or the second trigger are 13 (1), 12 (2), 10 (4), 9 (5) and
(6).

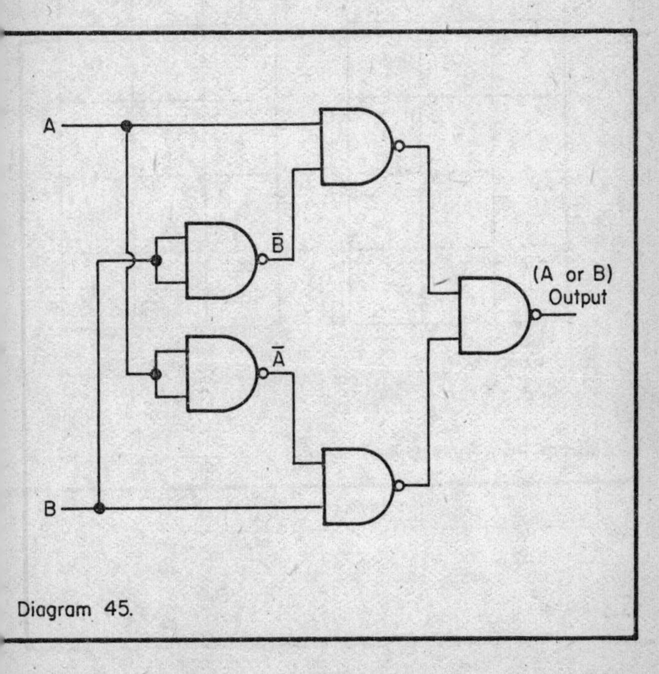

Diagram 45.

Circuit Thirty-Seven
EXCLUSIVE OR GATE

The circuit is for an "exclusive" OR gate, using five NAND gates. The difference between an exclusive OR gate (XOR) gate and a normal OR gate is that for an output of 1 the inputs can be A = 1, B = 1 or A and B = 1, but the XOR inputs are A = 1 or B = 1 *only*. See the two truth tables for OR and XOR gates (diagram 46). The circuit diagram for the XOR gate is diagram 45.

Note the use of inverters for cross coupling.

OR

Inputs 1	2	Output
0	0	0
1	0	1
0	1	1
1	1	1

XOR

Inputs 1	2	Output
0	0	0
1	0	1
0	1	1
1	1	0 *

* note difference

Diagram 46. Truth tables.

Circuit Thirty-Eight
DIVIDE BY SIX 7490 CIRCUIT

The 7490 is a useful ÷ 10 frequency divider for use at frequencies up to a few MHz (see diagram 47). It can be considered as a ÷ 2 and ÷ 5 circuit usually connected in cascade ÷ 2 then ÷ 5 to give the ÷ 10 function. However by altering the connections between the connecting pins from the normal arrangement, the 7490 can be used to divide by 2, 3, 4, 5, 6, 7, 8, 9 or 10, by setting the point at which the internal counter resets to zero. When used as a ÷ 10 counter it is connected so that the circuit counts up to 10 and then returns to zero.

The example used in this circuit is six, the counter is set to stop counting at 1010 and then return to 0000, 1010 is the binary equivalent of 6.

This mode of operation is very useful for electronic clock circuits with a 50 Hz reference input:

divide by 5 then 10 = 1 pulse per second;
divide by 6 then 10 = 1 pulse per minute;
divide by 6 then 10 = 1 pulse per hour;
divide by 6 then 4 = 1 pulse per day.

(An electronic clock is a good classroom project. Of course complete clock circuits are available in one I.C., but an electronic clock can be divided into a number of sub-circuits each to be completed by one pupil or pair, e.g. sections above:

(i) ÷ 50 circuit
(ii) ÷ 60 circuit
(iii) ÷ 60 circuit
(iv) ÷ 24 circuit
(v) power supply
(vi) display
(vii) 50 Hz reference pulse shaping circuit.)

Note that the power supply connections to the 7490 are different: pin 5 is 5V+; pin 10 is 0V (see diagram 47).

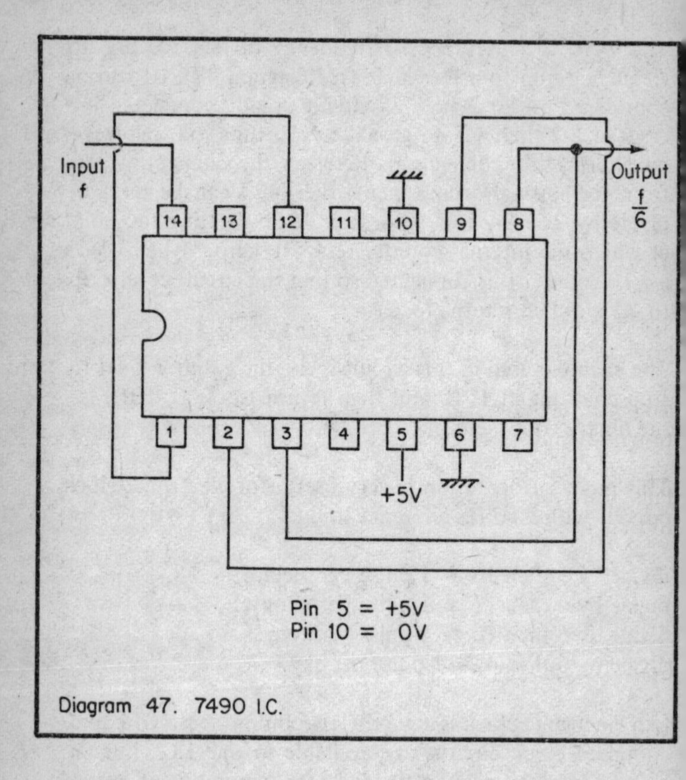

Diagram 47. 7490 I.C.

The 7490 contains four counter stages: Q1, Q2, Q3 and Q4. Outputs are:

Q1	12	2^0
Q2	9	2^1
Q3	8	2^2
Q4	11	2^3

The counter also has four control pins: 2 and 3 reset to 0; 6 and 7 reset to 9. The circuit is connected so that a pulse from Q2 and Q3 resets the counter, i.e. when the state of count is :

Q4	Q3	Q2	Q1	, to zero.
0	1	1	0	

Circuit Thirty-Nine
74121 PULSE GENERATOR

This is a circuit using a 74121 monostable circuit as a single high speed pulse generator. Each time the button is pressed a single pulse of 0.5 μsec (half a microsecond) duration is generated.

The pulse length depends on the values of R and C connected to pins 10 and 11 (C) and 9 (R).

Pulse duration $\triangleq$ 0.7 CR, where C is in Farads, R is in ohms. In this case:

$$C = 330 \text{ pF}$$
$$R = 2.2 \text{ K}\Omega.$$

Converting units to ohms and Farads:

$$C = 330 \times 10^{-12} \text{ F}$$
$$R = 2.2 \times 10^{3}\,\Omega.$$

$T \triangleq 330 \times 10^{-12} \times 2.2 \times 10^{3} \times 0.7$ seconds. If we multiply by 10^{6} this gives the answer in microseconds.

$$T \triangleq 330 \times 10^{-12} \times 2.2 \times 10^{3} \times 10^{6} \times 0.7.$$
$$T \triangleq 330 \times 2.2 \times 10^{-3} \times 0.7.$$
$$T \triangleq 0.5082.$$

The time is approximately only, resistors have a tolerance of 5%, capacitors 10% or more.

The time can easily be altered by using different values of C, e.g. if a 0.680 pF capacitor is used the time duration is about 1 microsecond or 1 μsec (see diagram 48).

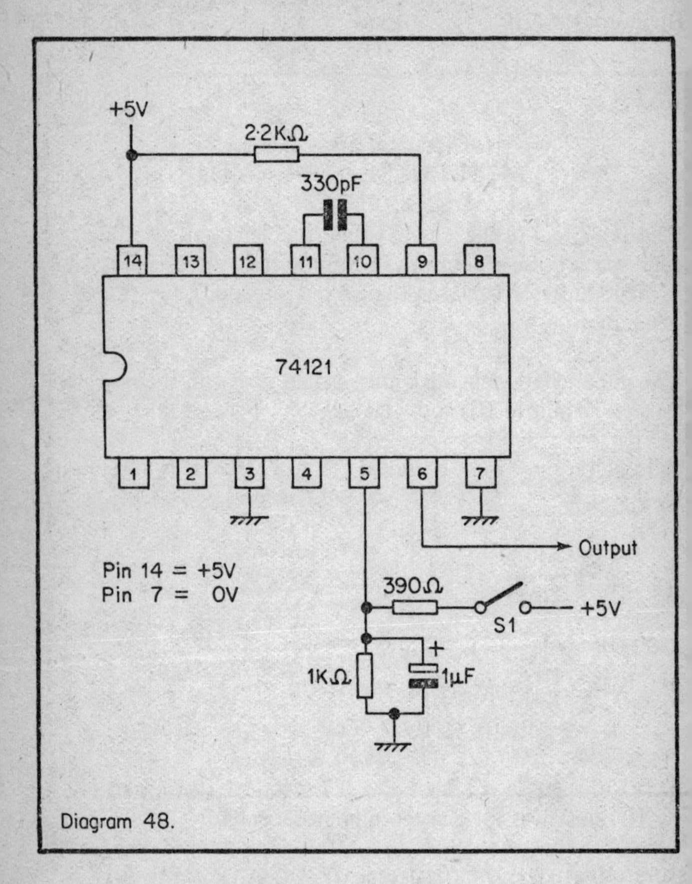

Diagram 48.

Circuit Forty
LOGIC SWITCH

This circuit is identical in action to a S.P.D.T. switch but here the switching is electronic and not mechanical and can work at very high speed. C is the control signal.

The output is A if C = 0, output is B if C = 1 (see diagram 49).

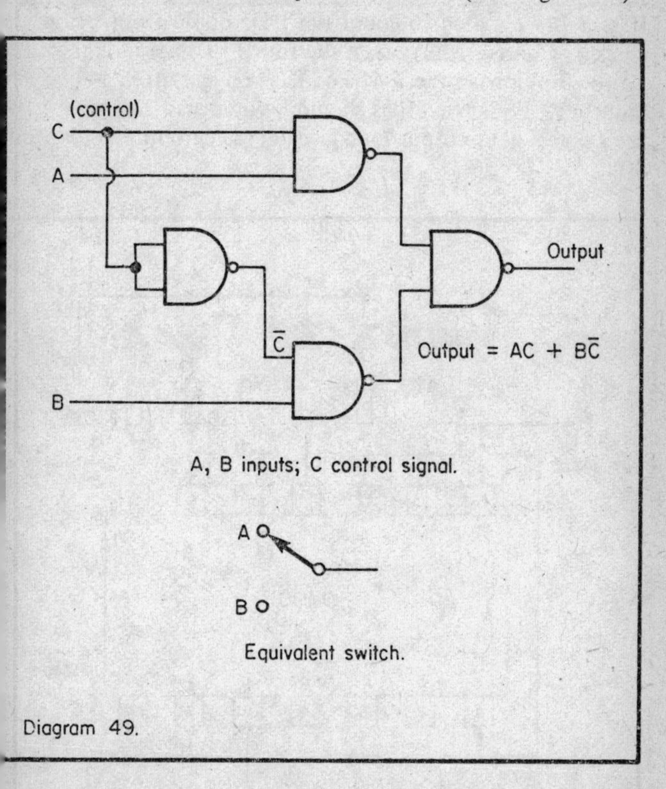

Diagram 49.

Fc NAND gates are used. C controls the gating of A, whereas an inverter gives the complement $\overline{C}$ (not C) to control B o that the output can be labelled:

$$AC + B\overline{C}$$

he small diagram shows the equivalent mechanical switch. In act the direct mechanical equivalent would be a relay, where control voltage operated the relay which switched between and B.

Circuit Forty-One
BINARY DISPLAY

Here a 7490 is used to count the 1 Hz pulses from a slow clock (e.g. circuit thirty-six), the four LEDs are illuminated via the flip-flops in the 7490 and flash on and off in a binary sequence. Four red LEDs should be used, red LEDs have the greatest light output for a given diode current (see diagram 50).

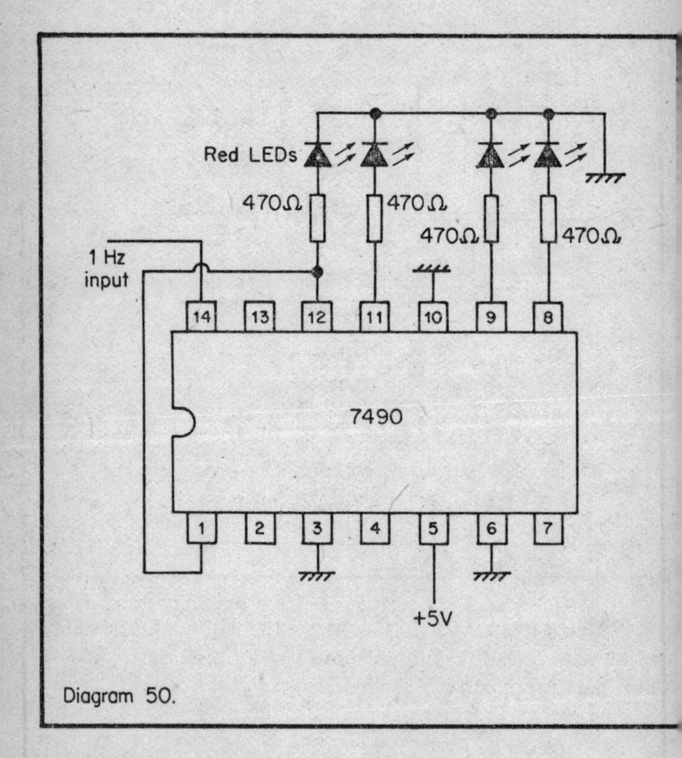

Diagram 50.

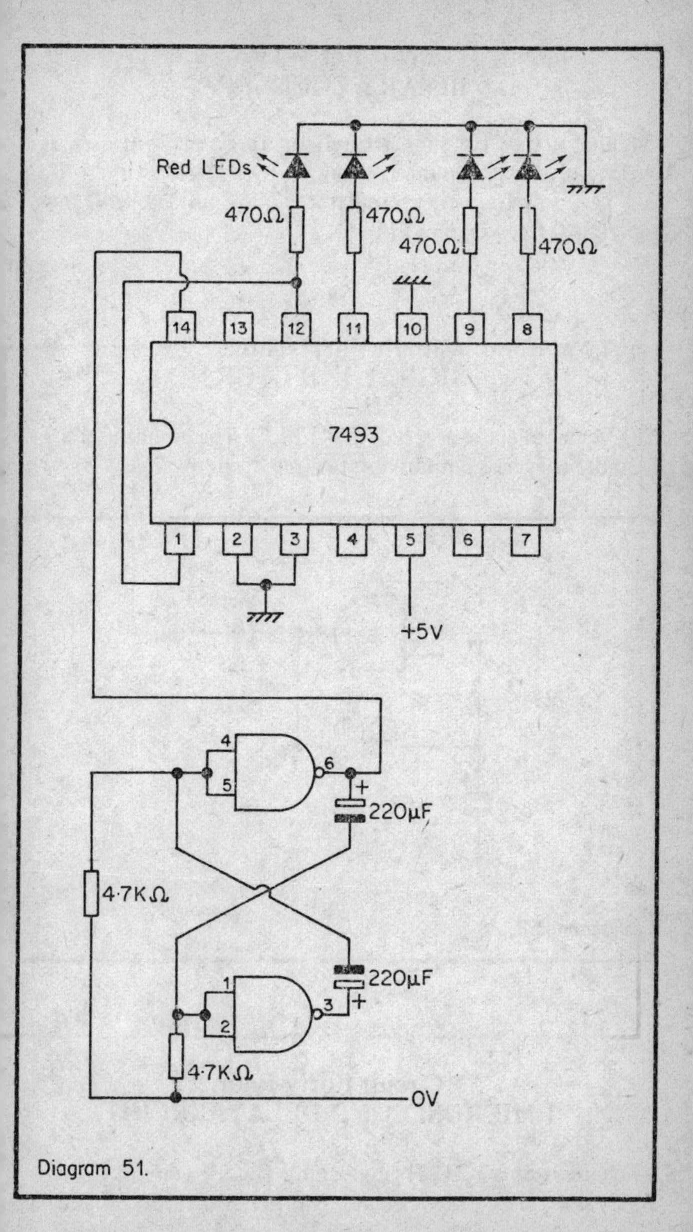
Red LEDs
470Ω
470Ω
470Ω
470Ω
14
13
12
11
10
9
8
7493
1
2
3
4
5
6
7
+5V
4
5
6
+
220μF
4·7KΩ
220μF
1
2
3
+
4·7KΩ
0V
Diagram 51.

Circuit Forty-Two
BINARY COUNTER

Circuit forty-two is similar to circuit forty-one, but uses a 7493 4-bit binary counter, and two NAND gates of a 7400 as a very low frequency oscillator. 7493 pin 5 is +5V and pin 10 is 0 (see diagram 51).

Circuit Forty-Three
SIGNAL INJECTOR

This signal injector uses half a 7413 I.C. The circuit uses a Schmitt trigger as a multivibrator (see diagram 52).

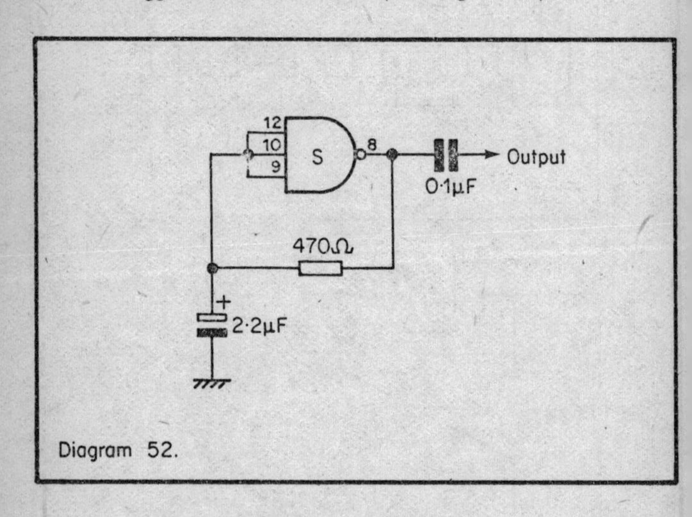

Diagram 52.

Circuit Forty-Four
1 MICROSECOND DELAY CIRCUIT

The circuit uses a 74121 monostable (refer to circuit thirty-nine) as a 1 μsec delay circuit. The 74121 is set to produce a pulse width of 1 μsec. The output pulse is differentiated to give 2 pulses, one at the beginning, one at the end of the 1 μsec period.

If a negative pulse triggers the monostable another negative pulse will appear at the differentiater output 1 μsec later. The 1N4148 high speed diode blocks off the positive pulse (see diagram 53).

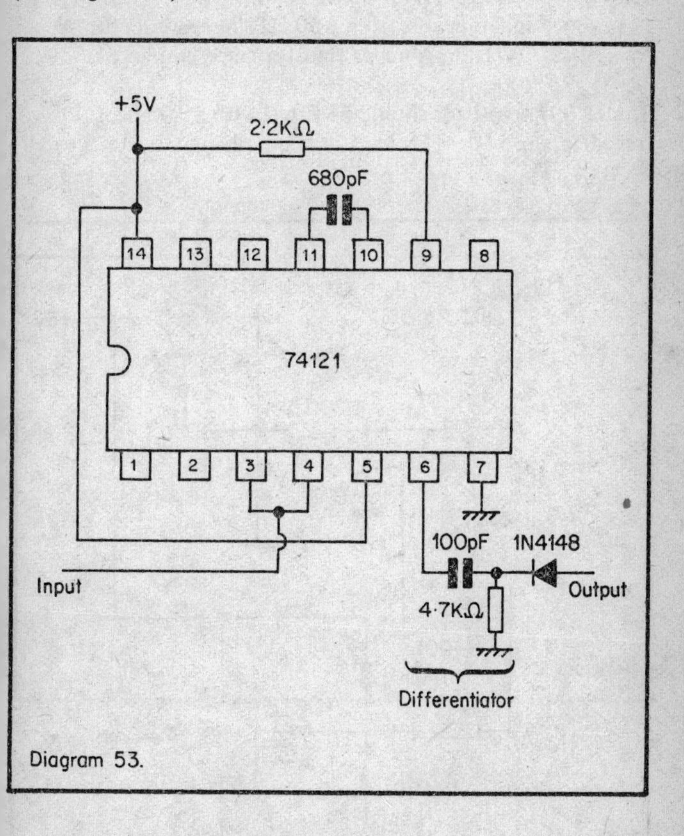

Diagram 53.

Circuit Forty-Five
SIMPLE 5V POWER SUPPLY AND 50 Hz SQUARE WAVE GENERATOR

This is a simple 5V power supply which can power 2 or 3 I.C.s and also includes a 50 Hz square wave generator.

The square wave generator uses a Schmitt trigger (I.C. 7413) to produce square waves from a 50 Hz sine wave input. A small 9–0–9V 100mA mains transformer is employed.

The 2N697 transistor should be fitted with a T05 heat sink (see diagram 54). The rectifiers are silicon 50 piv type 1N4001.

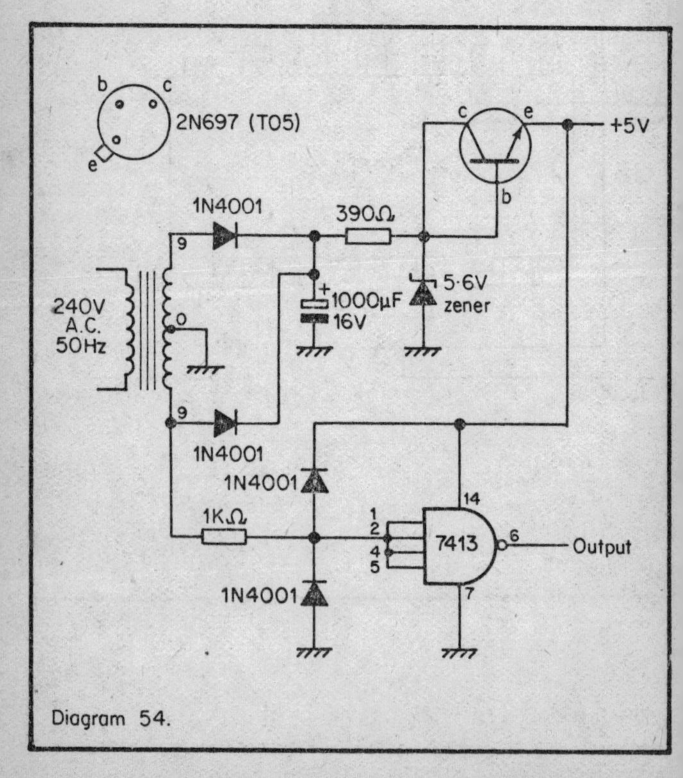

Diagram 54.

Circuit Forty-Six
LOGICAL PUZZLE

There is an old puzzle concerning a prisoner, two guards and two doors. One door leads to freedom, the other door leads to death. One guard always tells the truth, the other guard always lies. The prisoner is allowed to ask one question of one of the guards and must then proceed through one of the doors. What is the question?

Looking closely at the question we can see several binary situations. One of two doors, life or death, truth or lie.

The problem can be represented as a series of logic gates.

The doors can be labelled 1 and 0. The guard who lies can be a "NOT" gate and the guard who tells the truth can be

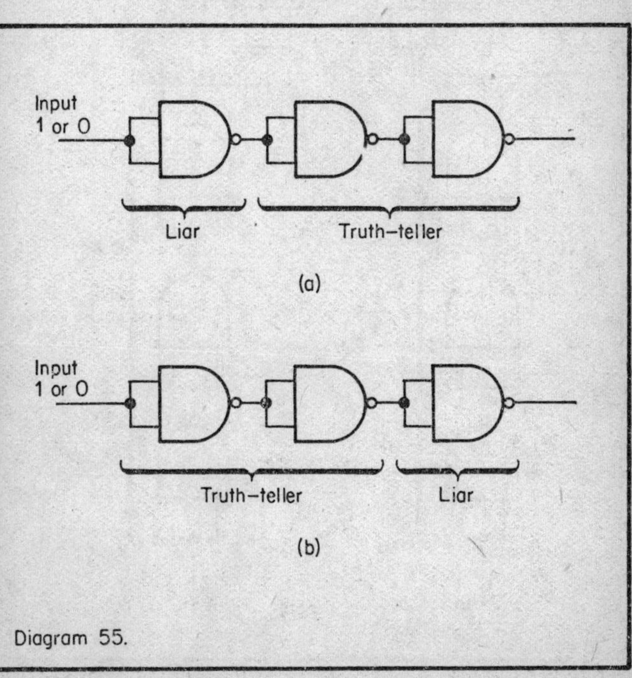

Diagram 55.

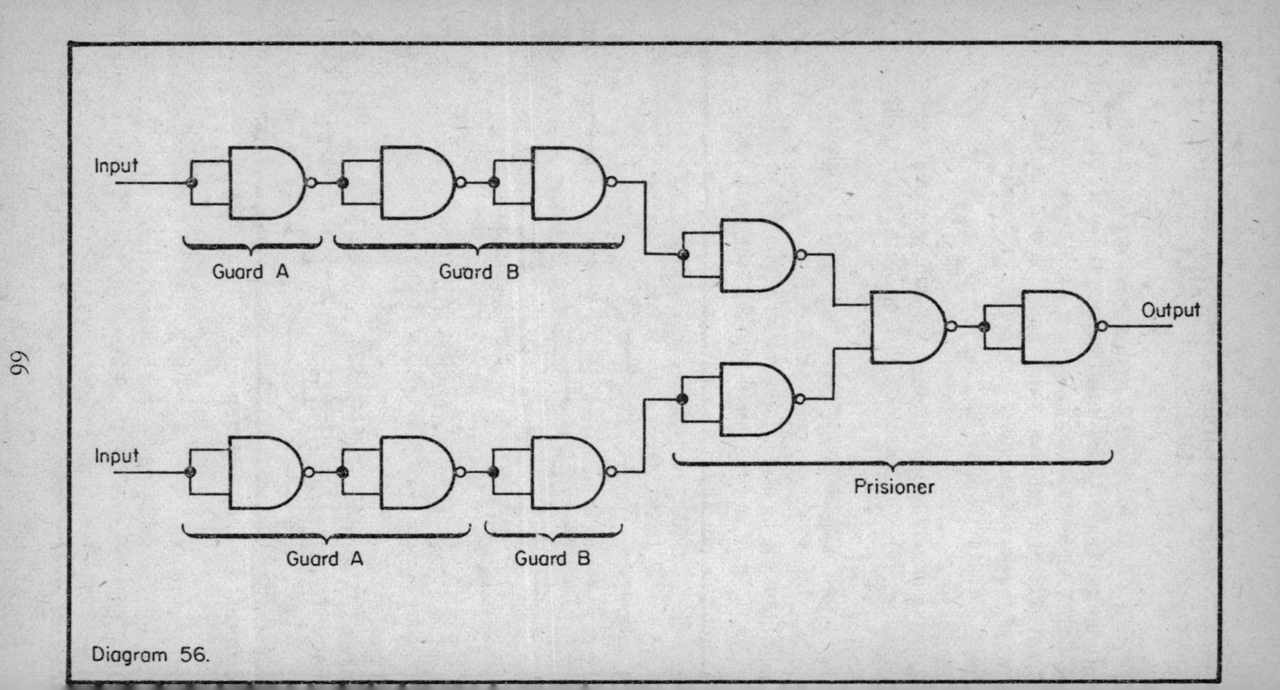

Diagram 56.

2 "NOT" gates in series, i.e. someone who does NOT NOT tell the truth.

The breakthrough in the problem is to realise that the information must involve both guards, i.e. ask one guard what the other one would say. Represent this by diagram 55(a) and 55(b). The information is either 1 or 0. If one guard is asked "What would the other guard say if asked which is the door to freedom?", the situation is either 55a *or* 55b. The prisoner does not know which but in a or b the logic process is the same.

An inversion takes place, the answer given to the prisoner is the opposite of the correct one. Hence if the prisoner functions as a NOT gate, he takes the opposite of the given answer, and this is the number of the door to freedom.

A circuit to indicate either situation requires an OR gate as the answer is NOT the one given by the guard a NOR gate is used.

Diagram 56 represents both situations, the input represents the number of the door.

Circuit Forty-Seven
HALF ADDER DESIGN

A greater understanding of the function of a half adder circuit may be obtained by examining the Truth table for the addition of two binary numbers – see Truth table diagram 57.

Note that in the dotted box the A, B inputs and the sum are identical to the function of a NAND gate.

Examine the Truth table again, more closely; see diagram 58. The function inside the dotted box is identical to the exclusive OR (XOR) function and the carry table is *almost* the inverse of the sum, so that the function is almost XOR + NOT (for the carry table). The half adder is XOR + NOT except when

digits

A	B	Sum	Carry
0	0	0	0
0	1	1	
1	0	1	
1	1	0	

Dotted box function = NAND.

Diagram 57. Binary addition truth table.

A	B	Sum	Carry
0	0	0	0
0	1	1	0
1	0	1	0
1	1	0	1

Dotted box = XOR function.
Carry is almost inverse of Sum
except when A = B = 0.

Diagram 58.

A and B are 0, then the sum and carry are 0. Or to rephrase:

NOT 0 AND 0
NOT AND is NAND,

so that the function of a half adder consists of XOR plus NOT plus NAND (see diagram 59). Compare with diagram 36. The drawings are slightly different, but they are *logically* identical.

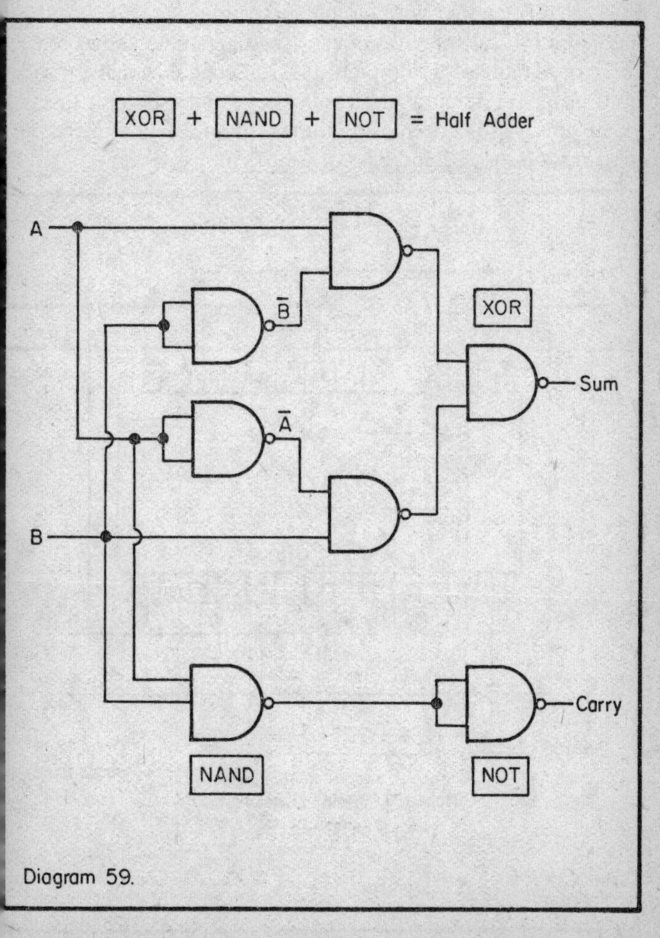

Diagram 59.

Circuit Forty-Eight
DIVIDE BY 4, IN QUADRATURE OUTPUTS CIRCUIT

This is an advanced application which uses a 7473 Dual Master Slave J.K. flip-flop, to generate two frequencies in quadrature, i.e. there is a 90° phase difference. The input frequency is four times the output frequencies.

This circuit together with circuit forty-nine V.C.O. forms the basis of a P.L.L. stereo decoder. The diagram 63 shows the skeleton circuit of a complete P.L.L. decoder which can be built using T.T.L. circuits. It must be emphasised that this is an advanced project requiring the use of an oscilloscope – see diagrams 60, 61, 62 and 63.

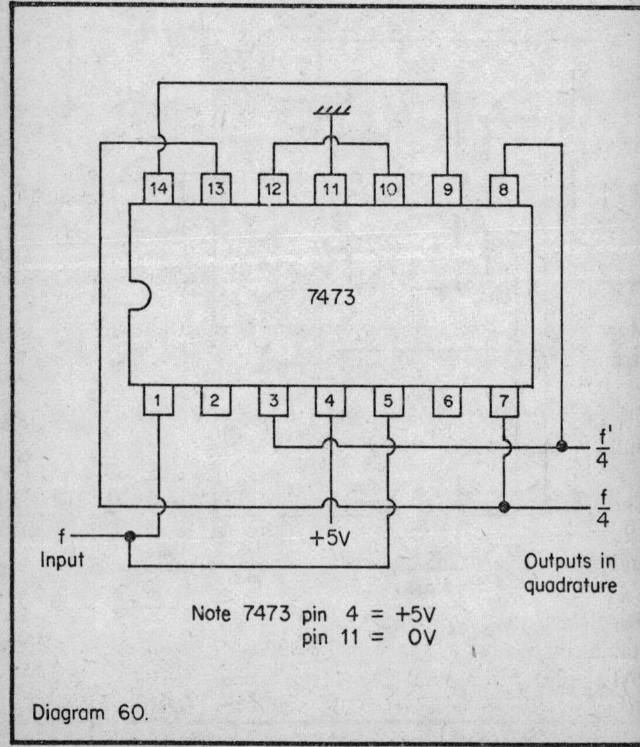

Diagram 60.

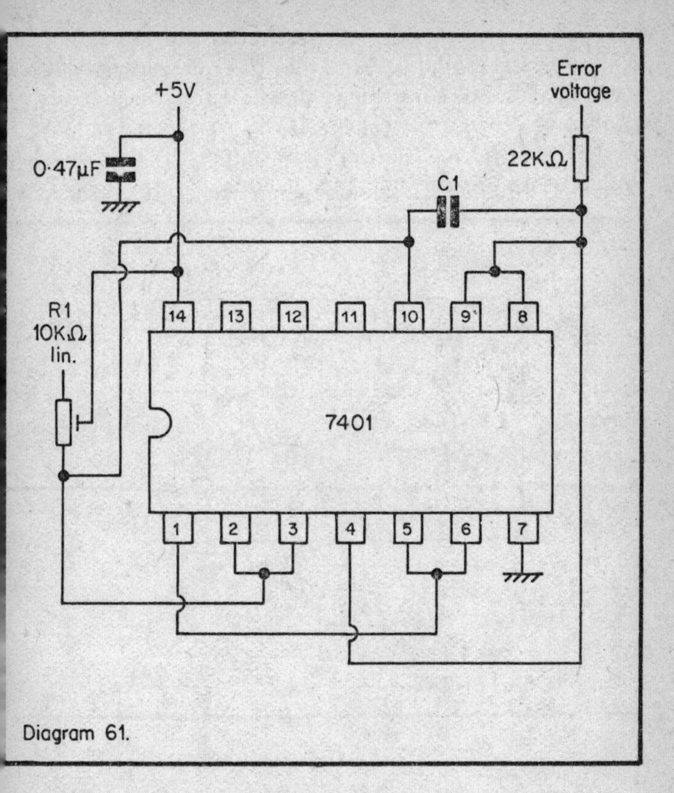

Diagram 61.

Most of the required circuits are featured in this book, constructors will have to design the decoding matrix themselves.

The circuit suggested is similar to the MC1310, but anyone can build a decoder using the MC1310!

The V.C.O. operates at 76 kHz. Circuit 48 produces two 19 kHz ops, one of these is locked onto the 19 kHz pilot tone and the error voltage controls the 76 kHz V.C.O.

For those who wish to experiment further, the 74121 monostable can be used as a low distortion F.M. demodulator. The 74121 time period must be set to less than the time occupied by one cycle at 10.7 MHz (I.F. frequency). If the I.F. is heavily limited so that the input is a series of pulses around 10.7 MHz, level about 0.5V, to the 74121 the output will be a series of pulses of constant width where frequency corresponds to the audio frequency. If this is fed via a suitable INTEGRATING R.C. network, the output will be a precise replica of the original audio modulation.

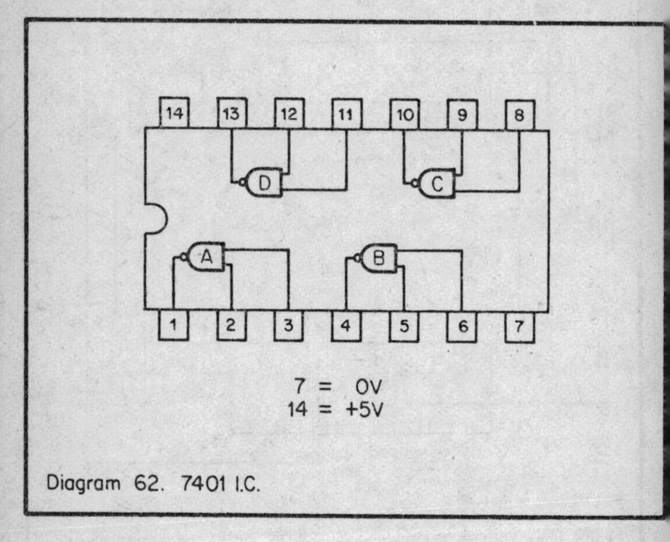

Diagram 62. 7401 I.C.

Circuit Forty-Nine
EXPERIMENTERS V.C.O.

This is an experimental V.C.O. (voltage controlled oscillator) which will work at frequencies up to several MHz by altering the value of C1. For use in a P.L.L. stereo decoder the nominal frequency is 76 kHz. Try C1 at 2200 pF to 4700 pF. R1 is the fine frequency control. The error voltage from the phase detector is fed via the 22 kΩ resistor (see diagram 31). This is an experimental circuit and may require adjustment of circuit values in order to achieve best performance, in particular C1 may vary and be outside the range indicated. The 7401 I.C. used is a four 2-input NAND gate I.C., which

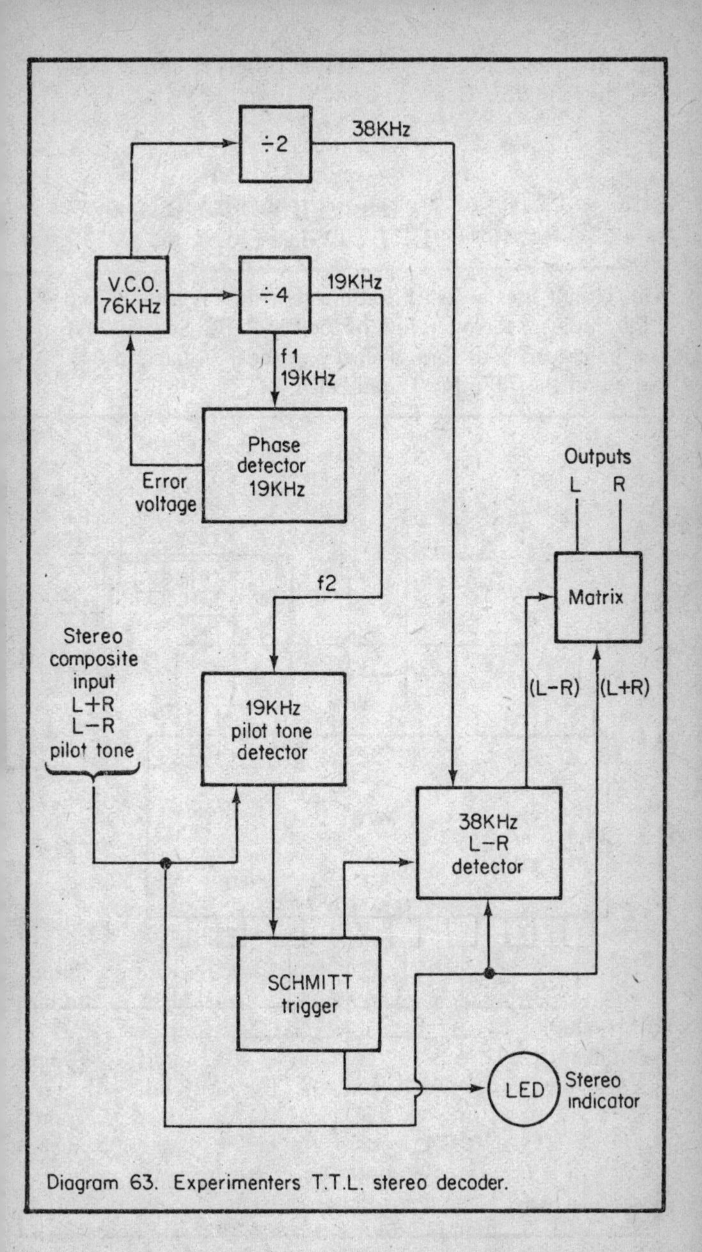

Diagram 63. Experimenters T.T.L. stereo decoder.

has an "open collecter" output and differs from the 7400 (see diagram 62). Gates A, B and C form the V.C.O.

Circuit Fifty
SHIFT REGISTER

This circuit uses a dual Flip-Flop in a shift register. Two LEDs indicate the operation of the flip-flops. Several 7476s can be cascaded to form a shift register (see diagram 64). Note that the 7476 is a 16-pin D.I.L. I.C.

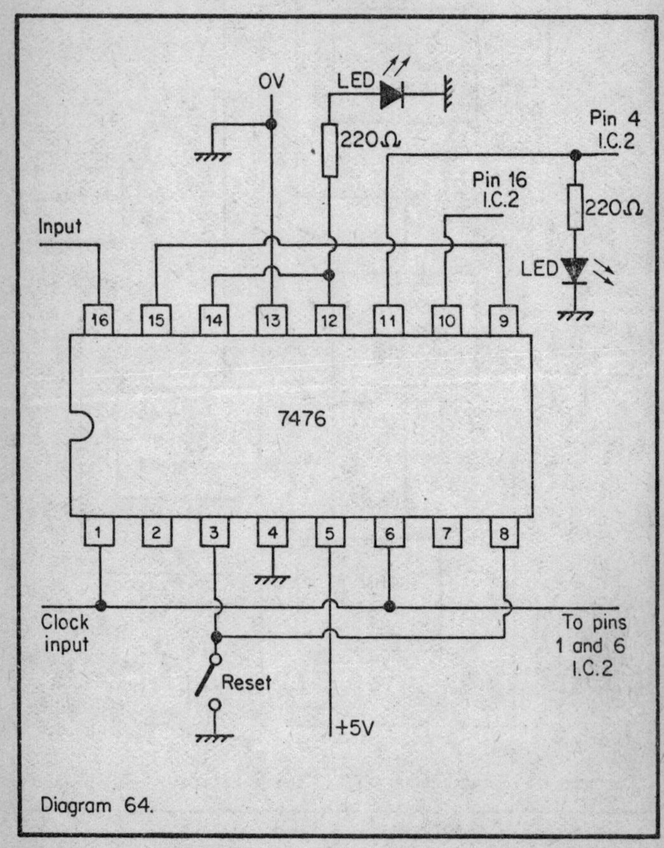

Diagram 64.

LIST OF I.C. TYPES USED

7400	Quad 2 input NAND
7401	Quad 2 input NAND open collecter
7402	Quad 2 input NOR
7404	Hex inverter (NOT)
7408	Quad 2 input AND
7413	Dual 4 input NAND Schmitt trigger
7473	Dual Master Slave J.K. Flip-Flop
*7476	Dual Master Slave J.K. Flip-Flop
7490	Decade Counter
7493	4-bit Binary Counter
74121	Monostable Flip-Flop

* 16-pin type. The remainder are 14-pin D.I.L.

ACKNOWLEDGEMENTS

The author would like to thank the following companies for help and information given while preparing the material for this book.

Codespeed Ltd.
Concept Electronics Ltd.
National Semiconductor Co. Ltd.
P.B. Electronics (Scotland) Ltd.
Vero Electronics Ltd.

Notes

OTHER BOOKS OF INTEREST

BP36: 50 CIRCUITS USING GERMANIUM SILICON AND ZENER DIODES
AUTHOR: R.N. SOAR — **PRICE: 75p**
ISBN: 0 85934 039 2 — 64 Pages
Approx. Size: 180 x 105 mm

Contains 50 interesting and useful circuits and applications, covering many different branches of electronics, using one of the most simple and inexpensive of components – the diode. Includes the use of germanium and silicon signal diodes, silicon rectifier diodes and zener diodes, etc. A valuable addition to the library of both the beginner and more advanced enthusiast alike.

BP42: 50 SIMPLE L.E.D. CIRCUITS
AUTHOR: R.N. SOAR — **PRICE: 75p**
ISBN: 0 85934 043 4 — 64 Pages
Approx. Size: 180 x 105 mm

The author of this book, Mr. R.N. Soar, has compiled 50 interesting and useful circuits and applications, covering many different branches of electronics, using one of the most inexpensive and freely available components – the Light Emitting Diode (L.E.D.). Also includes circuits for the 707 Common Anode Display. A useful book for the library of both beginner and more advanced enthusiast alike. Companion volume to book No. BP36 – 50 CIRCUITS USING GERMANIUM, SILICON & ZENER DIODES by the same author.

Please note overleaf is a list of other titles that are available in our range of Radio and Electronics Books.

These should be available from all good Booksellers, Radio Component Dealers and Mail Order Companies.

However, should you experience difficulty in obtaining any title in your area, then please write directly to the publisher enclosing payment to cover the cost of the book plus adequate postage.

If you would like a complete catalogue of all our Radio and Electronics Books then please send a Stamped Addressed Envelope to:

BERNARD BABANI (publishing) LTD
THE GRAMPIANS
SHEPHERDS BUSH ROAD
LONDON W6 7NF
ENGLAND

BP1	First Book of Transistor Equivalents and Substitutes	50p
BP2	Handbook of Radio, TV and Ind. & Transmitting Tube & Valve Equiv.	60p
BP6	Engineers and Machinists Reference Tables	50p
BP7	Radio and Electronic Colour Codes and Data Chart	25p
BP11	Practical Transistor Novelty Circuits	40p
BP14	Second Book of Transistor Equivalents	1.10p
BP22	79 Electronic Novelty Circuits	75p
BP23	First Book of Practical Electronic Projects	75p
BP24	52 Projects using IC741	95p
BP25	How to Build Your Own Electronic and Quartz Controlled Watches & Clocks	85p
BP26	Radio Antenna Handbook for Long Distance Reception & Transmission	85p
BP27	Giant Chart of Radio Electronic Semiconductor & Logic Symbols	60p
BP28	Resistor Selection Handbook (International Edition)	60p
BP29	Major Solid State Audio Hi-Fi Construction Projects	85p
BP30	Two Transistor Electronic Projects	85p
BP31	Practical Electrical Re-wiring & Repairs	85p
BP32	How to Build Your Own Metal and Treasure Locators	1.00p
BP33	Electronic Calculator Users Handbook	95p
BP34	Practical Repair & Renovation of Colour TV's	95p
BP35	Handbook of IC Audio Preamplifier & Power Amplifier Construction	95p
BP36	50 Circuits Using Germanium, Silicon and Zener Diodes	75p
BP37	50 Projects Using Relays, SCR's and TRIAC's	1.10p
BP38	Fun & Games with your Electronic Calculator	75p
BP39	50 (FET) Field Effect Transistor Projects	1.25p
BP40	Digital IC Equivalents and Pin Connections	2.50p
BP41	Linear IC Equivalents and Pin Connections	2.75p
BP42	50 Simple L.E.D. Circuits	7 p
BP43	How to make Walkie-Talkies	1.25p
BP44	IC 555 Projects	1.45p
BP45	Projects on Opto-Electronics	1.25p
BP46	Radio Circuits using IC's	1.35p
BP47	Mobile Discotheque Handbook	1.35p
BP48	Electronic Projects for Beginners	1.35p
BP49	Popular Electronic Projects	1.45p
BP50	IC LM3900 Projects	1.35p
BP51	Electronic Music and Creative Tape Recording	1.25p
BP52	Long Distance Television Reception (TV–DX) for the Enthusiast	1.45p
BP53	Practical Electronic Calculations and Formulae	2.25p
BP54	Your Electronic Calculator and Your Money	1.35p
BP55	Radio Stations Guide	1.45p
BP56	Electronic Security Devices	1.45p
BP57	How to Build your own Solid State Oscilloscope	1.50p
BP58	50 Circuits using 7400 Series IC's	1.35p
BP59	Second Book of CMOS IC Projects	1.50p
BP60	Practical Construction of Pre-Amps. Tone Controls. Filters and Attenuators	1.45p
BP61	Beginners Guide to Digital Techniques	95p
100	A Comprehensive Radio Valve Guide – Book 1	40p
121	A Comprehensive Radio Valve Guide – Book 2	40p
126	Boys Book of Crystal Sets	25p
138	How to Make Aerials for TV (Band 1–2–3)	25p
143	A Comprehensive Radio Valve Guide – Book 3	40p
157	A Comprehensive Radio Valve Guide – Book 4	40p
160	Coil Design and Construction Manual	75p
178	A Comprehensive Radio Valve Guide – Book 5	40p
196	AF–RF Reactance – Frequency Chart for Constructors	15p
200	Handbook of Practical Electronic Musical Novelties	50p
201	Practical Transistorised Novelties for Hi-Fi Enthusiasts	35p
202	Handbook of Integrated Circuits (IC's) Equivalents and Substitutes	1.00p
203	IC's and Transistor Gadgets Construction Handbook	60p
205	First Book of Hi-Fi Loudspeaker Enclosures	75p
206	Practical Transistor Circuits for Modern Test Equipment	60p
207	Practical Electronic Science Projects	75p
208	Practical Stereo and Quadrophony Handbook	75p
210	The Complete Car Radio Manual	1.00p
211	First Book of Diode Characteristics Equivalents and Substitutes	95p
213	Electronic Circuits for Model Railways	1.00p
214	Audio Enthusiasts Handbook	85p
215	Shortwave Circuits and Gear for Experimenters and Radio Hams	85p
216	Electronic Gadgets and Games	1.00p
217	Solid State Power Supply Handbook	85p
218	Build Your Own Electronic Experimenters Laboratory	85p
219	Solid State Novelty Projects	85p
220	Build Your Own Solid State Hi-Fi and Audio Accessories	85p
221	28 Tested Transistor Projects	95p
222	Solid State Short Wave Receivers for Beginners	95p
223	50 Projects using IC CA3130	95p
224	50 CMOS IC Projects	95p
225	A Practical Introduction to Digital IC's	95p
226	How to Build Advanced Short Wave Receivers	1.20p
227	Beginners Guide to Building Electronic Projects	1.25p
228	Essential Theory for the Electronics Hobbyist	1.25p
RCC	Resistor Colour Code Disc Calculator	10p